Contents

Contents
The Ultimate Book of Second Grade Skills, SV 9781419099533

Features

The *Ultimate Book of Second Grade Skills* is the perfect resource to help parents stay involved in their child's learning process and to help busy teachers enhance children's learning in their classrooms. The book can be used as practice and reinforcement for children in second grade and for those who have just completed second grade. It can also be utilized as a stepping stone for children entering second grade.

The 224-page comprehensive book provides grade-appropriate, skills-based practice in the four core subject areas—

- language arts
- math
- science
- social studies

The practice pages cover essential second grade skills in a short practice format that is not overwhelming for children to help ensure understanding. The practice pages can be completed in any order.

In addition to the practice pages, there are several other important features of this book.

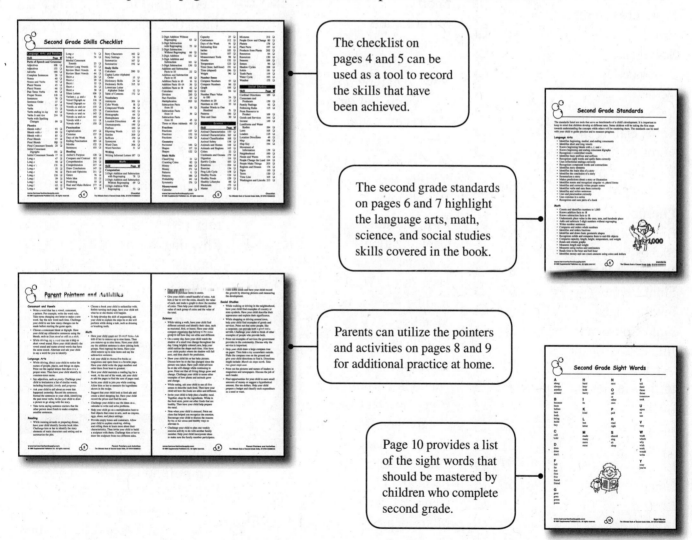

The checklist on pages 4 and 5 can be used as a tool to record the skills that have been achieved.

The second grade standards on pages 6 and 7 highlight the language arts, math, science, and social studies skills covered in the book.

Parents can utilize the pointers and activities on pages 8 and 9 for additional practice at home.

Page 10 provides a list of the sight words that should be mastered by children who complete second grade.

On page 218, you will find a certificate to present to the child when the book has been completed. A bound-in answer key follows the certificate.

Second Grade Skills Checklist

Checklist
The Ultimate Book of Second Grade Skills, SV 9781419099533

Science

Social Studies

Checklist
The Ultimate Book of Second Grade Skills, SV 9781419099533

Second Grade Standards

The standards listed are tools that serve as benchmarks of a child's development. It is important to keep in mind that children develop at different rates. Some children will be taking the first steps towards understanding the concepts while others will be mastering them. The standards can be used with your child to guide practice and to measure progress.

Language Arts

- Identifies beginning, medial, and ending consonants
- Identifies short and long vowels
- Knows beginning blends with *s, l,* and *r*
- Knows beginning and ending consonant digraphs
- Recognizes *r*-controlled vowels
- Identifies basic prefixes and suffixes
- Recognizes sight words and spells them correctly
- Uses inflectional endings correctly
- Recognizes compound words and contractions
- Identifies story elements
- Identifies the main idea of a story
- Identifies the conclusion of a story
- Summarizes a story
- Makes predictions about a story or illustration
- Identifies nouns and recognizes singular vs. plural forms
- Identifies and correctly writes proper nouns
- Identifies verbs and uses them correctly
- Identifies and writes sentences
- Uses end punctuation correctly
- Uses commas in a series
- Recognizes and uses parts of a book

Math

- Counts and identifies numbers to 1,000
- Knows addition facts to 18
- Knows subtraction facts to 18
- Understands place value in the ones, tens, and hundreds place
- Adds and subtracts 3-digit numbers without regrouping
- Writes number sentences
- Compares and orders whole numbers
- Identifies and orders fractions
- Identifies and draws basic geometric shapes
- Recognizes solids and compares them to real-life objects
- Compares capacity, length, height, temperature, and weight
- Reads and creates graphs
- Measures length and weight
- Measures using inches and centimeters
- Reads time to the hour and half-hour
- Identifies money and can count amounts using coins and dollars

- Sequences events
- Knows time passage (days, weeks, months, yesterday, next week)
- Uses a calendar
- Uses problem-solving strategies to complete math problems
- Understands basic probability

Science

- Understands the difference in living and nonliving things
- Recognizes characteristics of living things
- Sorts organisms according to their characteristics
- Recognizes that living things function, adapt, and change
- Understands characteristics and functions of plants and their parts
- Understands characteristics and functions of animals and their parts
- Classifies organisms
- Identifies the life cycles of organisms
- Uses senses to explore and observe the environment
- Names major body parts
- Makes comparisons among objects that have been observed
- Describes basic needs of living things, like air and water
- Identifies how people use resources
- Identifies ways that people can take care of Earth
- Recognizes patterns in nature
- Describes the water cycle
- Begins to understand forces
- Recognizes that shadows change length and positions during the day
- Recognizes the states of matter and how they change
- Describes good health habits
- Identifies healthy food choices
- Identifies major organs of the body and their functions

Social Studies

- Explains the significance of community, state, and national celebrations
- Identifies contributions of historical figures
- Identifies basic cardinal directions
- Identifies locations on a map
- Identifies major land formations and water bodies
- Describes how land formations affect land settlement and activities
- Explains how work provides income for goods and services
- Recognizes that people have jobs to earn money
- Recognizes that people exchange goods and services
- Describes differences in producing and consuming
- Describes the development of a product from natural resource to finished product
- Recognizes functions of government
- Identifies functions of a community
- Identifies characteristics of a good citizen
- Describes movement of information
- Recognizes how people change the land
- Identifies leaders in the home, school, community, state, and nation
- Understands that voting is a way that people make choices

The Ultimate Book of Second Grade Skills, SV 9781419099533

Parent Pointers and Activities

Consonant and Vowels

- Write a word that has a vowel, consonant, *e* pattern. For example, write the word *rake*. Take turns changing one letter to make a new word. Say the new word each time. Challenge your child to see how many changes can be made before starting the game again.

- Choose a consonant blend or digraph. Have your child say alliterative sentences using the blends, such as *Stan stood as still as a stick.*

- While driving, say a word that has a long or short vowel sound. Have your child identify the vowel sound and name several words that have the same sound. Alternate and ask your child to say a word for you to identify.

Language Arts

- While driving, direct your child to notice the names of people, places, and things on signs. Point out the capital letters that show it is a proper noun. Then have your child identify its common-noun name.

- Say adjectives, such as *pretty*. Challenge your child to brainstorm a list of similar words, including *beautiful, lovely,* and *gorgeous.*

- Ask your child to tell about an event that happened yesterday. Record the sentences. Reread the sentences to your child, identifying the past tense verbs. Invite your child to draw a picture to go along with the story.

- Take turns saying sentence starters that the other person must finish to make complete, sensible sentences.

Reading

- While running errands or preparing dinner, have your child identify favorite book titles. Challenge him or her to identify the story elements of main characters and setting and to summarize the plot.

- Choose a book your child is unfamiliar with. Before turning each page, have your child tell what he or she thinks will happen.

- To help develop the skill of sequencing, ask your child to explain the steps he or she will perform while doing a task, such as dressing or brushing teeth.

Math

- Have your child count out 18 small items. Ask him or her to remove up to nine items. Then you remove up to nine items. Have your child say the addition sentence to show joining both groups. Next regroup the items. Have your child remove up to nine items and say the subtraction sentence.

- Ask your child to choose five books or magazines and open them to a favorite page. Have your child write the page numbers and order them from least to greatest.

- Have your child maintain a reading log for a week. At the end of the week, ask your child to add the pages to find the sum of pages read.

- Invite your child to join you while cooking. Allow him or her to measure the ingredients shown in the recipe.

- Suggest that your child look at food ads and create a short shopping list. Have your child record the prices and find the sum.

- Challenge your child to use the dates on a calendar to write and solve problems.

- Help your child go on a multiplication hunt to find objects that come in sets, such as crayons, eggs, shoes, and place settings.

- Provide empty boxes and containers. Allow your child to explore stacking, sliding, and rolling them to learn more about their characteristics. Then invite your child to build a sculpture with them. Challenge him or her to draw the sculpture from two different sides.

- Have your child count out the coins and bills needed to purchase items in stores.
- Give your child a small handful of coins. Ask him or her to sort the coins, identify the value of each, and make a graph to show the number of coins. Then help your child identify the value of each group of coins and the value of the total.

Science

- While taking a walk, have your child find different animals and identify their class, such as mammal, bird, or insect. Have your child compare organisms that belong to the same group to tell how they are alike and different.
- On a sunny day, have your child watch the shadow of a small tree change throughout the day. Using brightly colored yarn, help your child outline the shape each time. Also have your child predict where the shadow will fall next, and then check the prediction.
- Show your child his or her baby picture. Discuss how he or she has changed since the picture was taken. Have your child tell how he or she will change while continuing to grow. Point out that all living things grow and change. Challenge your child to name other examples of how plants and animals grow and change.
- While eating, ask your child to use all five senses to describe each food. Then have your child tell how the foods are alike and different.
- Invite your child to help plan a healthy meal. Together, shop for the ingredients. While in the food store, point out other foods that are healthy. Then have your child help prepare the meal.
- Note when your child is stressed. Point out clues that helped you recognize the emotion. Encourage your child to discuss the reasons for his or her stress and healthy ways to alleviate it.
- Challenge your child to plan one weekly exercise activity to do with another family member. Help your child incorporate ideas to make sure the family member participates.
- Plant some seeds and have your child record the growth by drawing pictures and measuring the development.

Social Studies

- While walking or driving in the neighborhood, have your child find examples of country or state symbols. Have your child describe their appearance and explain their significance.
- While shopping or driving around town, help your child find examples of goods and services. Point out that some people, like a carpenter, can provide both a good and a service. Challenge your child to think of other examples of people who provide both.
- Point out examples of services the government provides in the community. Discuss why the service is important.
- Help your child draw a large compass rose on paper. Then hide a toy somewhere outside. Place the compass rose on the ground and give your child directions to find it. Directions might include: *March six steps north. Take two giant steps east.*
- Point out the pictures and names of leaders in magazines and newspapers. Discuss the job of each leader.
- Find opportunities for your child to earn small amounts of money or suggest a hypothetical amount, like ten dollars. Help your child prepare a budget and classify each expenditure as a need or want.

Second Grade Sight Words

A
along
always
another
around

B
because
been
before
best
both
bring
build
buy

C
call
cold

D
does
done
don't

F
fall
far
fast
first
five
found
friend

G
gave
goes
green
guess

H
hard
hear
hold
hurry

I
its

K
kind

L
last
letter

M
made
many
more
most

N
next

O
off
or
other
own

P
pull

R
read
right

S
should
sing
sit
sleep

T
tell
their
these
those
tomorrow
took

U
upon
us
use

V
very

W
wash
which
why
wish
work
would
write

Y
your
you're

Sight Words
The Ultimate Book of Second Grade Skills, SV 9781419099533

Name That Pattern

Directions Write your name in the boxes below so that one letter is in each box. Keep writing your name over and over until you fill all of the boxes. Look to see if there is a pattern.

Dot-to-Dot Alphabet

Directions Draw lines to join the dots from _a_ to _z_ to complete the picture. Then color the picture.

Here, Spot!

Directions Write the missing numbers. Then draw spots on the dog to match the number. Draw a line to match the number to the number word.

1 ____ ____ 4 ____ ____ ____ ____ 9 ____ ____

12 ____ ____ ____ ____ 17 ____ ____ ____

		eight		
9				17
		fifteen		
15		two		13
		seventeen		
19		six		8
		nine		
2		twelve		16
		nineteen		
12		four		6
		thirteen		
4		seven		20
		twenty		
7		one		1
		sixteen		

Numbers to 20
The Ultimate Book of Second Grade Skills, SV 9781419099533

A Good Fit

Directions Color the picture that answers each question.

1. Which hat will fit best in the box?

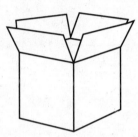   

2. Which shoe will fit best on the foot?

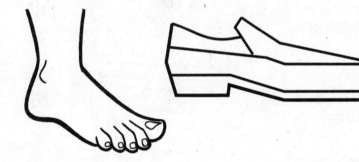  

3. Which doghouse is the best fit for the dog?

Estimating Size
The Ultimate Book of Second Grade Skills, SV 9781419099533

Alphabet Mystery

Directions Write the letter that comes **next**.

1. R   S   ○—◇

2. J   K   _____

3. D   ○—◇

4. Q   R   ○—◇

B   _____

F   G   ○—◇

J   K   _____

U   V   _____

Directions Write the letter that comes **before**.

5. _____   X   Y

6. ○—◇   B   C

7. ○—◇   S   T

8. _____   L   M

○—◇   U   V

_____   G   H

_____   E   F

○—◇   G   H

Directions Write the letter that comes in the **middle**.

9. P _____ R

10. R   ○—◇   T

H   ○—◇   J

G   ○—◇   I

Directions Write the letters in the magnifying glasses in order to answer the riddle.

What sea animal is a famous actor?

___ ___ ___ ___ ___ ___ ___ ___

Capital Letter Alphabet Order
The Ultimate Book of Second Grade Skills, SV 9781419099533

Name _____ Date _____

Sweet Dream Facts

Directions Add. Color the squares with an even sum red. Color the squares with an odd sum blue.

Remember

An even number ends with 0, 2, 4, 6, or 8.

An odd number ends with 1, 3, 5, 7, or 9.

1. $5 + 2$	2. $1 + 3$	3. $3 + 6$	4. $7 + 1$	5. $3 + 5$
6. $6 + 3$	7. $2 + 8$	8. $4 + 4$	9. $3 + 1$	10. $2 + 7$
11. $0 + 8$	12. $1 + 6$	13. $5 + 2$	14. $3 + 4$	15. $5 + 5$
16. $2 + 3$	17. $2 + 4$	18. $6 + 1$	19. $8 + 2$	20. $3 + 3$

Addition Facts to 10
The Ultimate Book of Second Grade Skills, SV 9781419099533

Name _____ Date _____

Sound Off!

Directions Write the letter that stands for the first sound in each picture name.

1. _____	2. _____	3. _____
4. _____	5. _____	6. _____
7. _____	8. _____	9. _____
10. _____	11. _____	12. _____
13. _____	14. _____	15. MILK _____

Initial Consonant Sounds
The Ultimate Book of Second Grade Skills, SV 9781419099533

Name _____ Date _____

Color Mixing

Directions Unscramble the color words. Write one letter in each space.

1. dre   2. aegnor   3. nipk   4. regen

5. lube   6. dlgo   7. wyeoll

1. ◯ ___ ___ ___

2. ___ ___ ◯ ___ ___ ___

3. ___ ◯ ___ ___ ___

4. ___ ___ ___ ◯ ___

5. ◯ ___ ___ ___

6. ___ ◯ ___ ___

7. ___ ___ ___ ___ ◯ ___

Directions Write the letters in the circles in order to complete the sentence.

A _____ is caused by the sun shining through tiny drops of water in the air.

Snacking on Facts

Directions Subtract.

1. 9
  − 3

2. 6
  − 2

3. 8
  − 5

4. 9
  − 4

5. 8
  − 2

6. 10
  − 7

7. 6
  − 3

8. 7
  − 2

9. 10
  − 6

10. 5
  − 0

11. 4
  − 3

12. 6
  − 6

13. 9
  − 7

14. 8
  − 4

15. 10
  − 2

19

Subtraction Facts from 10
The Ultimate Book of Second Grade Skills, SV 9781419099533

Lasting Sounds

Directions Write the letter that stands for the last sound in each picture name.

1. ___	2. ___	3. ___
4. ___	5. ___	6. ___
7. ___	8. ___	9. ___
10. ___	11. ___	12. ___
13. ___	14. ___	15. ___

Final Consonant Sounds
The Ultimate Book of Second Grade Skills, SV 9781419099533

Name _____   Date _____

Pairing Up

Directions Which pictures are alike? Write the name of a picture from the box beside something that is like it. Write a sentence to tell how the two are alike.

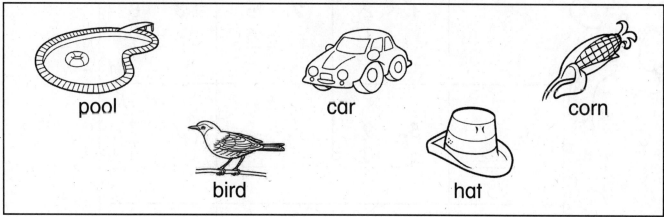

pool

car

corn

bird

hat

1. _____

_____

_____

2. _____

_____

_____

3. _____

_____

_____

4. _____

_____

5. _____

_____

Classifying
The Ultimate Book of Second Grade Skills, SV 9781419099533

Mixing Up Math

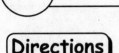

Directions Add or subtract.

1. 2 + 1	**2.** 6 − 6	**3.** 8 − 0
4. 7 + 2	**5.** 9 − 3	**6.** 2 + 6	**7.** 7 − 4
8. 8 − 4	**9.** 5 + 3	**10.** 9 + 1	**11.** 10 − 6
12. 4 + 5	**13.** 9 − 6	**14.** 8 − 3	**15.** 2 + 3
16. 10 − 3	**17.** 6 + 2	**18.** 4 + 5	

Addition and Subtraction Facts to 10
The Ultimate Book of Second Grade Skills, SV 9781419099533

In the Middle

Directions Write the letter that stands for the middle sound in each picture name.

1. le _____ on	2. tu _____ tle	3. pa _____ er
4. li _____ ard	5. sho _____ el	6. ro _____ ot
7. ca _____ oe	8. bo _____ es	9. wa _____ on
10. spi _____ er	11. me _____ al	12. ca _____ el

Medial Consonant Sounds
The Ultimate Book of Second Grade Skills, SV 9781419099533

Name _____ Date _____

Note the Order

Number the words in ABC order. Then write the words in ABC order.

1. _2_ bat   **1.** _____
   _1_ air   **2.** _____
   _3_ cat   **3.** _____

5. ___ yes   **1.** _____
   ___ zoo   **2.** _____
   ___ x-ray   **3.** _____

2. ___ neck   **1.** _____
   ___ owl   **2.** _____
   ___ mail   **3.** _____

6. ___ hat   **1.** _____
   ___ jump   **2.** _____
   ___ in   **3.** _____

3. ___ top   **1.** _____
   ___ sea   **2.** _____
   ___ rock   **3.** _____

7. ___ egg   **1.** _____
   ___ fish   **2.** _____
   ___ dog   **3.** _____

4. ___ well   **1.** _____
   ___ us   **2.** _____
   ___ vase   **3.** _____

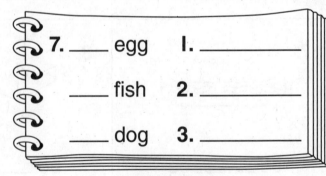

Dictionary Skills
The Ultimate Book of Second Grade Skills, SV 9781419099533

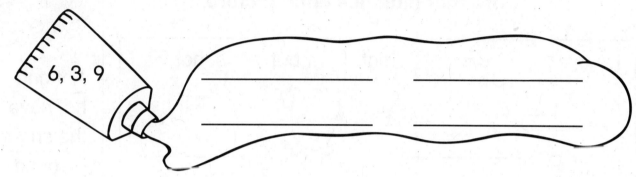

Painting Fact Families

Directions Write the fact families.

1.
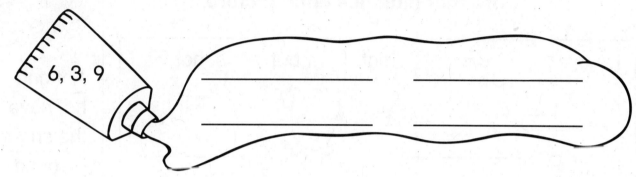

6, 3, 9

_____ _____

_____

2.
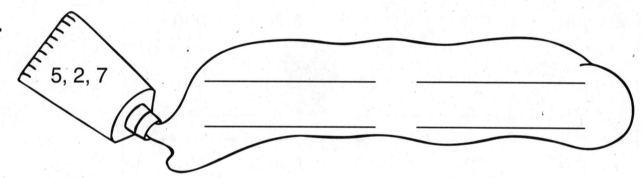

5, 2, 7

_____ _____

_____

3.
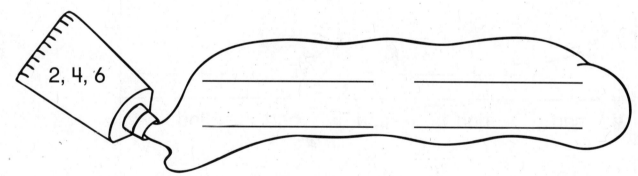

2, 4, 6

_____ _____

_____

4.

7, 3, 10

_____ _____

_____

Fact Families
The Ultimate Book of Second Grade Skills, SV 9781419099533

Name _____ Date _____

Some Words About <u>Short a</u>

Directions Read the **short a** words. Then write the word that **matches each picture.**

I. sat   cat   mat   bat   hat

_____   _____

---

2. fan   ran   can   man   pan

_____   _____

---

3. map   tap   lap   nap   cap

_____   _____

---

4. sad   dad   mad   bad   lad

_____   _____

---

5. tag   wag   rag   sag   bag

_____   _____

Fill 'er Up

Directions Circle the best estimate.

1. 	less than a cup about a cup more than a cup	**2.** 	less than a cup about a cup more than a cup
3. 	less than a cup about a cup more than a cup	**4.** 	less than a cup about a cup more than a cup
5. 	less than 5 gallons about 5 gallons more than 5 gallons	**6.** 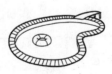	less than 5 gallons about 5 gallons more than 5 gallons
7.	less than 5 gallons about 5 gallons more than 5 gallons	**8.**	less than 5 gallons about 5 gallons more than 5 gallons

A Frog Surprise

Directions Read each group of words.
Write <u>yes</u> if the words are a
sentence. Write <u>no</u> if they are
not a sentence.

> **Remember**
> A sentence is a
> complete thought.

1. I walked by a lake. _____

2. A frog. _____

3. It sat by the lake. _____

4. I caught it with my hands. _____

5. took it home. _____

6. I showed it to my mom. _____

7. Jumped away. _____

8. Mom was very surprised. _____

Directions Which groups of words above did not make a
sentence? Write them so they are sentences.

_____

_____

_____

The Ultimate Book of Second Grade Skills, SV 9781419099533

Name _____ Date _____

Picture Some <u>Short e</u> Words

Directions Read the <u>short e</u> words. Then write the word that matches each picture.

Remember

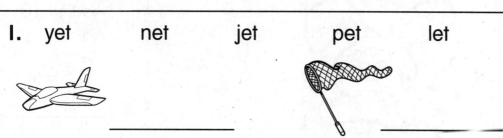

<u>Egg</u> and <u>hen</u> have the short e sound.

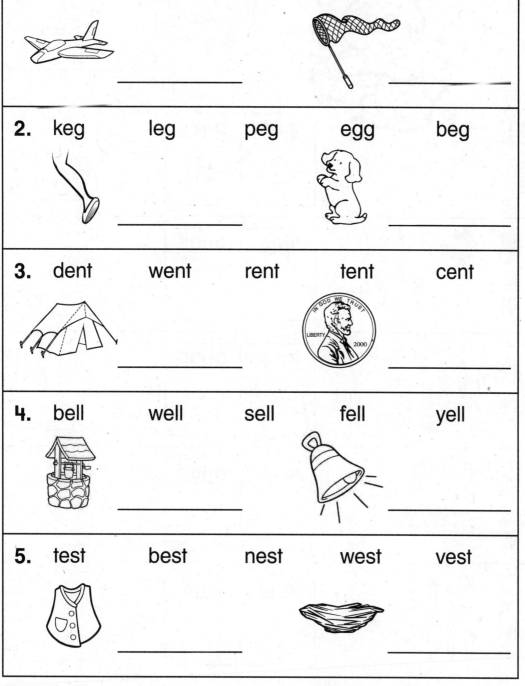

1. yet   net   jet   pet   let

_____   _____

2. keg   leg   peg   egg   beg

_____   _____

3. dent   went   rent   tent   cent

_____   _____

4. bell   well   sell   fell   yell

_____   _____

5. test   best   nest   west   vest

_____   _____

Short e
The Ultimate Book of Second Grade Skills, SV 9781419099533

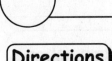

Name _____ Date _____

Crazy for Carrots

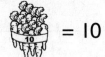

Directions Write how many tens and ones.
Then write the number.

Remember

= 10

= 1

1.

tens	ones
2	5

25

2.

tens	ones

_____

3.

tens	ones

_____

4.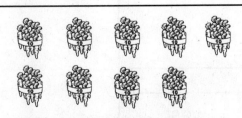

tens	ones

_____

5.

tens	ones

_____

Tens and Ones
The Ultimate Book of Second Grade Skills, SV 9781419099533

Name _____   Date _____

Fun with Word Families

Directions Say each picture name. Change the first letter of each word. Write the picture name.

1.	2.	3.
cat	pen	mug
____at	____en	____ug
____at	____en	____ug
____at	____en	____ug

Word Families
The Ultimate Book of Second Grade Skills, SV 9781419099533

Is It **Short i?**

Directions Circle the pictures with the
short i sound.

> **Remember**
>
>
>
> **Ink** and **fish** have
> the **short i** sound.

1.

2.

3.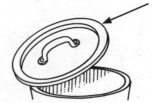

4.

Short *i*
The Ultimate Book of Second Grade Skills, SV 9781419099533

Ants at a Picnic

Directions Write the missing numbers.

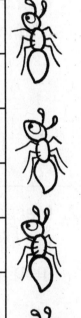

1				5					
					16				
		23							
			34						40
				45					
		53							
									70
			74						
					86				
		93							

Numbers to 100
The Ultimate Book of Second Grade Skills, SV 9781419099533

Guess the Setting

Directions Read each story. Where does each story take place? Color the picture.

Remember
The setting is where the story takes place.

1. Ben sat up in bed and rubbed his eyes. Then he looked at the clock. "I'm late!" he yelled. Ben quickly jumped out of bed.

2. Mei sat down on a bench. She had already seen the monkeys and the lions. Now she wanted to see the elephants. Mei looked at a map to find out where they were.

3. The students lined up by the door. Soon the teacher walked to the front of the line and went out of the classroom. The students followed behind.

Some Words About <u>Short o</u>

Directions Read the <u>short o</u> words. Then write the word that matches each picture.

Remember

Ox and <u>mop</u> have the short o sound.

1.	lock	mock	rock	sock	dock

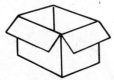 _____

 _____

2.	hop	pop	mop	cop	top

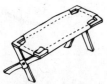 _____

 _____

3.	box	fox	lox	ox	pox

 _____

_____

4.	cot	not	dot	pot	tot

_____

_____

5.	fog	dog	log	bog	cog

_____

_____

Balls of Fun with Facts

Directions Add.

1. 5
   + 7

5. 6
   + 6

9. 5
   + 6

13. 9
    + 4

2. 9
   + 1

6. 9
   + 5

10. 3
    + 9

14. 7
    + 7

3. 8
   + 3

7. 4
   + 8

11. 8
    + 4

15. 2
    + 9

4. 7
   + 2

8. 8
   + 6

12. 7
    + 7

Addition Facts 10–14
The Ultimate Book of Second Grade Skills, SV 9781419099533

Name _____   Date _____

Sentences with Sense

Directions Write each group of words to make a sentence that makes sense.

Remember

A sentence begins with a capital letter and has an ending mark.

1. is Fred friend My

_____

2. likes He run to

_____

3. He last a week had race.

_____

4. winning was Fred

_____

5. shoelace came His loose

_____

6. Fred and fell tripped

_____

7. win not did Fred race the

_____

Name _____ Date _____

Thumbs Up for <u>Short u</u>

Directions Write <u>u</u> if the picture name has the <u>short u</u> sound.

1. _____	2. _____	3. _____	4. _____
5. _____	6. _____	7. _____	8. _____
9. _____	10. _____	11. _____	12. _____
13. _____	14. _____	15. _____	16. _____

The Ultimate Book of Second Grade Skills, SV 9781419099533

Name _____   Date _____

Stopping for the Facts

Directions **Subtract.**

1.
$$11 - 3$$

5.
$$10 - 2$$

9.
$$14 - 6$$

13.
$$11 - 9$$

2.
$$13 - 5$$

6.
$$12 - 6$$

10.
$$9 - 4$$

14.
$$12 - 5$$

3.
$$9 - 6$$

7.
$$14 - 9$$

11.
$$13 - 8$$

15.
$$14 - 8$$

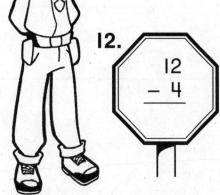

4.
$$12 - 8$$

8.
$$11 - 7$$

12.
$$12 - 4$$

16.
$$13 - 6$$

Subtraction Facts from 14
The Ultimate Book of Second Grade Skills, SV 9781419099533

Name _____   Date _____

Finding Nouns

Directions Circle the two nouns in each sentence.

1. The children walk out of the classroom.

2. The playground is behind the school.

3. The teacher carries a ball.

4. The friends run to the swings.

5. A girl jumps rope.

Directions Look at the words you circled above. Do they name a person, a place, or a thing? Write the words in the correct column.

Person	Place	Thing

Name _____   Date _____

A Short Review

Directions Color the pictures with names that have the short vowel sound of the letter in the box.

1. U

2. e

3. i

4. a

5. o

Review Short Vowels
The Ultimate Book of Second Grade Skills, SV 9781419099533

Name _____   Date _____

Tracking Facts

Directions Add.

1.
$$\begin{array}{r} 6 \\ + 7 \\ \hline \end{array}$$

5.
$$\begin{array}{r} 9 \\ + 7 \\ \hline \end{array}$$

9.
$$\begin{array}{r} 7 \\ + 6 \\ \hline \end{array}$$

12.
$$\begin{array}{r} 9 \\ + 8 \\ \hline \end{array}$$

2.
$$\begin{array}{r} 6 \\ + 5 \\ \hline \end{array}$$

6.
$$\begin{array}{r} 6 \\ + 8 \\ \hline \end{array}$$

10.
$$\begin{array}{r} 9 \\ + 9 \\ \hline \end{array}$$

13.
$$\begin{array}{r} 5 \\ + 9 \\ \hline \end{array}$$

3.
$$\begin{array}{r} 8 \\ + 8 \\ \hline \end{array}$$

7.
$$\begin{array}{r} 9 \\ + 5 \\ \hline \end{array}$$

11.
$$\begin{array}{r} 7 \\ + 7 \\ \hline \end{array}$$

14.
$$\begin{array}{r} 7 \\ + 8 \\ \hline \end{array}$$

4.
$$\begin{array}{r} 5 \\ + 6 \\ \hline \end{array}$$

8.
$$\begin{array}{r} 4 \\ + 8 \\ \hline \end{array}$$

Addition Facts to 18
The Ultimate Book of Second Grade Skills, SV 9781419099533

Name _____ Date _____

Seeing Double

Directions Look at the pictures.
Circle the correct noun.

Remember
Add s or es to nouns to show
more than one. Add es to words
ending in ch, s, sh, ss, or x.

1.

boy   boys   boyes

2.

cat   cats   cates

3.

peach   peachs   peaches

4.

lion   lions   liones

5.

dress   dresss   dresses

6.

rake   rakes   rakees

7.

clown   clowns   clownes

8.

car   cars   cares

Plural Nouns
The Ultimate Book of Second Grade Skills, SV 9781419099533

Mystery Messages

Directions Read each sentence. Write the same vowel in each word to complete the sentence.

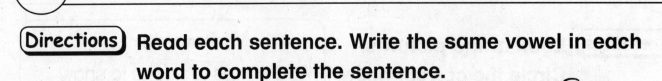

1. The d___ck had f___n in the wet m___d.

2. The c___t s___t on P___m's l___p.

3. J___n w___nt to g___t a p___t h___n.

4. The d___g h___ps ___n the l___g.

5. W___ll J___m's b___g f___sh w___n?

Parrot Facts

Directions Subtract. Then color the picture.

5 = orange	6 = red	7 = green	8 = blue	9 = yellow

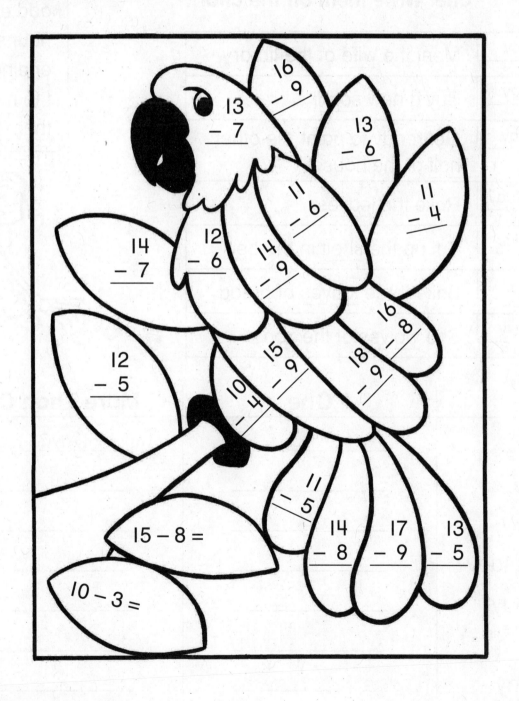

Subtraction Facts from 18
The Ultimate Book of Second Grade Skills, SV 9781419099533

Name _____ Date _____

A Busy Week

Directions Look at the underlined words. Change the plural nouns to mean one. Change the single nouns to mean more than one. Write them on the chart.

Remember
Change the f to v and add es to nouns ending in f to make them plural.

Sunday	Meet the <u>wife</u> at the library
Monday	Buy a new <u>scarf</u>
Tuesday	Get ready to paint the other <u>half</u> of the house
Wednesday	Rake the <u>leaves</u>
Thursday	Put up the <u>shelf</u> in the den
Friday	Bake three <u>loaves</u> of bread
Saturday	See <u>wolves</u> at the zoo

Day	One	More Than One
Sunday	wife	wives
Monday	_____	_____
Tuesday	_____	_____
Wednesday	_____	_____
Thursday	_____	_____
Friday	_____	_____
Saturday	_____	_____

Plural Nouns
The Ultimate Book of Second Grade Skills, SV 9781419099533

Name _____ Date _____

Word Change-Up

Directions Rewrite each word and add an <u>e</u>. Draw the picture that names the word.

Remember

cake

Long a can be spelled <u>a_e</u>.

1.

man
_____

_____

2.

pan
_____

_____

3.

tap
_____

_____

4.

cap
_____

_____

5.

Soup
can
_____

_____

6.

van
_____

_____

Directions Write a word from above to complete each sentence.

7. My granddad walks with a _____.

8. Mom needs _____ to wrap the gift.

9. The magician wears a long black _____.

Name _____   Date _____

Let It Snow Facts!

Directions Add or subtract.

Remember
Look at the sign to see
if you add or subtract.

1. 6
   + 9

5. 17
   − 9

9. 7
   + 7

13. 8
    + 8

16. 16
    − 9

2. 14
   − 8

6. 17
   − 8

10. 6
    + 8

14. 9
    + 9

17. 15
    − 7

3. 7
   + 7

7. 6
   + 7

11. 16
    − 7

15. 17
    − 8

18. 9
    + 8

4. 15
   − 6

8. 18
   − 9

12. 15
    − 8

www.harcourtschoolsupply.com

Addition and Subtraction Facts to 18
The Ultimate Book of Second Grade Skills, SV 9781419099533

Come Here, Ruff!

Directions **Read the directions to complete the picture.**

1. Color the doghouse brown.

2. Draw a tree to the left of the house.

3. Draw a bird nest in the tree.

4. Draw a dog to the right of the house.

5. Draw a red food dish in front of the house.

6. Draw a blue bird on top of the house.

Name _____   Date _____

Long a Patterns

Directions Circle the word that names the picture.

Remember

Long a has several spelling patterns.

cake   quail

tray

1.

hate   hail   hay

2.

tray   train   take

3.

pail   page   pay

4.

chain   cane   clay

5.

jay   jail   jade

6.

rain   rake   ray

7.

may   mane   mail

8.

whale   wait   way

Name _____ Date _____

Batting Practice

Directions Read each number word. Color the ball with the matching number.

1. seventeen

17   71

2. twenty-eight

28   29

3. thirty-four

34   43

4. fifty

15   50

5. seventy-six

76   67

6. ninety-six

69   96

7. eighty-nine

88   89

8. three

3   30

9. one hundred

10   100

10. sixty-six

66   61

Here's an Idea

Directions Look at each picture. Circle the sentence that tells about the picture.

1.	2.	3.

Leah reads a book.	The bird finds a worm.	Anna goes to the store.
Leah plays in the park.	The bird sits in a nest.	Anna gets on the bus.

Directions Read the paragraph. Circle the sentence that best tells what the paragraph is about.

4. Toys have been around for many years. The earliest toys were very simple. They were dolls and animal toys. They had no moving parts. Toys today often have many moving parts. They are very different from toys of the past.

Toys today often have many moving parts.

They were dolls and animal toys.

Toys have been around for many years.

Main Idea
The Ultimate Book of Second Grade Skills, SV 9781419099533

Name _____ Date _____

Which Street to Eat?

Directions Jean is at the post office. She wants to eat at the café. She will take the streets with words that have the <u>long e</u> sound. Draw a line to show Jean the way.

Remember

Long <u>e</u> has several spelling patterns.

leaf

bee

neck
rest
meal
creep
desk   jeep   queen   neat   green
heat
feel
seal
see
bent   neat   eat

Long e
The Ultimate Book of Second Grade Skills, SV 9781419099533

Monkeying Around with Numbers

Directions Circle the place value of each __underlined__ number.

1. 264

6 ones

6 tens

6 hundreds

4. 731

7 ones

7 tens

7 hundreds

2. 157

1 ones

1 tens

1 hundreds

5. 504

0 ones

0 tens

0 hundreds

3. 428

8 ones

8 tens

8 hundreds

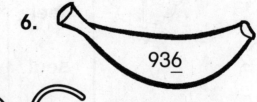

6. 936

6 ones

6 tens

6 hundreds

Number Place Value to 100
The Ultimate Book of Second Grade Skills, SV 9781419099533

Next?

Directions Read each story. What will happen next? Color
the picture.

1. Ken went to his room. He looked at the toys on the shelf. He saw
a ball, a top, a puzzle, and a jack-in-the-box. He picked up one of
the toys. Ken turned the handle slowly and then faster. He got ready
for a surprise.

2. Jill and her mother walked on the beach. The warm water washed
on Jill's feet. Jill suddenly put her pail down.

"Look, Mom!" said Jill. "Here is a pretty pink one lying in the sand."

Jill bent over to pick up something.

The Ultimate Book of Second Grade Skills, SV 9781419099533

Name _____   Date _____

Empty the Bank

Directions Use the code key to write a letter on each line.

a	b	c	d	e	f	g	h	i	j	k
1	2	3	4	5	6	7	8	9	10	11

l	m	n	o	p	q	r	s	t	u	v	w	x	y	z
12	13	14	15	16	17	18	19	20	21	22	23	24	25	26

1. ___ ___ ___ ___ ___
    6   21   14   14   25

2. ___ ___
    13   5

3. ___ ___ ___ ___ ___ ___
    19   17   21   5   1   12

4. ___ ___ ___ ___ ___
    16   9   7   7   25

5. ___ ___ ___ ___ ___
    8   1   16   16   25

6. ___ ___ ___ ___ ___
    7   18   5   5   4

7. ___ ___ ___ ___ ___
    13   15   14   5   25

8. ___ ___ ___ ___ ___ ___
    22   1   12   12   5   25

9. ___ ___
    8   5

10. ___ ___ ___ ___ ___
    5   13   16   20   25

The Ultimate Book of Second Grade Skills, SV 9781419099533

Name _____ Date _____

Winning Scores

Remember

\> means "is greater than."

< means "is less than."

14 ⊗ 7

1. 20 ◯ 50

2. 67 ◯ 61

3. 96 ◯ 95

4. 37 ◯ 42

5. 82 ◯ 72

6. 59 ◯ 60

7. 42 ◯ 24

8. 73 ◯ 72

9. 86 ◯ 88

10. 57 ◯ 45

11. 62 ◯ 64

12. 87 ◯ 78

13. 60 ◯ 50

14. 54 ◯ 53

15. 88 ◯ 99

16. 69 ◯ 70

Compare Numbers

The Ultimate Book of Second Grade Skills, SV 9781419099533

Picture These Words

Directions Write words that name the pictures. Then write the compound word made by the two words. Draw a picture to match the compound word.

Remember
A compound word is a long word made by joining two smaller words.

1.  **+**  **=**

   _____   _____   _____

2. **+** **=**

   _____   _____   _____

3. **+** 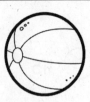 **=**

   _____   _____   _____

4. **+**  **=**

   _____   _____   _____

Compound Words
The Ultimate Book of Second Grade Skills, SV 9781419099533

Find Long i

Directions Say each picture name. Write i_e to complete the word if you hear the **long i** sound.

Remember

kite

Long i can be spelled i_e.

1. d i c e	2. b _ b	3. n _ n
4. h _ v	5. p _ g	6. s _ t
7. b _ k	8. p _ p	9. p _ n
10. d _ v	11. k _ t	12. v _ n

Name _____ Date _____

It All Adds Up

Directions Add.

1.
```
   2
   3
 + 4
```

5.
```
   6
   2
 + 5
```

9.
```
   2
   1
   4
 + 3
```

13.
```
   3
   4
   9
 + 2
```

2.
```
   4
   5
 + 1
```

6.
```
   7
   3
 + 4
```

10.
```
   4
   5
   5
 + 2
```

14.
```
   6
   3
   3
 + 5
```

3.
```
   3
   2
 + 3
```

7.
```
   9
   4
 + 1
```

11.
```
   7
   2
   3
 + 6
```

4.
```
   1
   3
 + 2
```

8.
```
   5
   5
 + 5
```

12.
```
   6
   0
   8
 + 3
```

The Ultimate Book of Second Grade Skills, SV 9781419099533

Name _____ Date _____

Home Sick

Directions Write a word from the box
that means the same as the
<u>underlined</u> word.

> friend   giggle   hat   hopped
> house   sad   sick   sleep   yell

Remember

Synonyms are
words that have
the same or
almost the same
meanings.

1. I was so <u>unhappy</u>. _____

2. I had to stay in bed because I was <u>ill</u>. _____

3. I had just begun to <u>doze</u>. _____

4. I heard someone <u>shout</u>. _____

5. I <u>jumped</u> out of bed. _____

6. It was my <u>pal</u> Ben. _____

7. He stood outside my <u>home</u>. _____

8. His dog did tricks to make me <u>laugh</u>. _____

Synonyms
The Ultimate Book of Second Grade Skills, SV 9781419099533

Tic-Tac-Toe

Directions Mike wants a kite. Cy wants a pie. Draw a kite or pie to see who wins. Then answer the question.

Remember

Long i has several spelling patterns.

kite   pie   fly

1. Draw a pie on lie.
2. Draw a kite on dry.
3. Draw a kite on try.
4. Draw a pie on die.
5. Draw a kite on my.
6. Draw a kite on tire.
7. Draw a kite on by.
8. Draw a pie on tie.

tie	my	bike
die	try	lie
by	dry	tire

Who wins? _____

Long i
The Ultimate Book of Second Grade Skills, SV 9781419099533

Name _____ Date _____

Penguin Adding

Directions Add.

> **Remember**
> First add the ones. Then add the tens.

1.

tens	ones
1	3
+	2

2.

tens	ones
2	4
+	3

3.

tens	ones
3	0
+	8

4.

tens	ones
3	2
+	7

5.

tens	ones
3	5
+ 1	4

6.

tens	ones
4	3
+ 3	4

7.

tens	ones
5	1
+ 1	0

8.

tens	ones
4	7
+ 1	2

9.   65
      + 24

10.   84
      + 13

11.   41
      + 47

12.   20
      + 30

13.   70
      + 19

14.   35
      + 42

15.   44
      + 53

16.   61
      + 25

Name _____ Date _____

Word Play

Directions Look at each pair of pictures. Read each sentence. Then write the letter of the correct meaning on the line.

Remember
A homograph is a word that has two or more meanings.

A.    **B.**

1. _____ Tom is taking a trip to visit his grandmother.

2. _____ Tie your shoelaces so that you will not trip over them.

3. _____ When will Pilar get back from her trip?

A.    **B.**

4. _____ Birds fly in the sky.

5. _____ Keep the fly off the food.

6. _____ That fly is bothering me.

Homographs
The Ultimate Book of Second Grade Skills, SV 9781419099533

Name _____ Date _____

I Have Mail

Directions Cross out the letters <u>A</u>, <u>C</u>, <u>J</u>, <u>P</u>, <u>U</u>, and <u>Z</u>. Write the message.

Remember

Long i has several spelling patterns.

kite   pie

fly   knight

S E E C J H O W A P Z

U M Y P B R I G H T C

K I T E A F L I E S J

I N Z T H E U P S K Y

Message _____

_____

Directions Write the words from the message in the correct column to show the <u>long i</u> spelling pattern. Write more words in each column to show the pattern.

1. i_e	2. ie	3. y	4. igh
_____	_____	_____	_____
_____	_____	_____	_____
_____	_____	_____	_____

Long *i*
The Ultimate Book of Second Grade Skills, SV 9781419099533

Sandy Subtraction

Directions Subtract.

> **Remember**
> First subtract the ones.
> Then subtract the tens.

1.
tens	ones
1	8
−	4

2.
tens	ones
2	6
−	3

3.
tens	ones
2	9
−	9

4.
tens	ones
4	3
−	2

5.
tens	ones
3	4
− 1	1

6.
tens	ones
4	7
− 1	4

7.
tens	ones
6	8
− 2	6

8.
tens	ones
5	6
− 3	5

9.   77
    − 26

10.   82
    − 40

11.   79
    − 57

12.   95
    − 33

13.   64
    − 14

14.   55
    − 22

15.   72
    − 61

16.   89
    − 73

2-Digit Subtraction Without Regrouping
The Ultimate Book of Second Grade Skills, SV 9781419099533

Name _____ Date _____

Get Going

Directions What is happening in each picture? Write a verb from the box. Then circle the pictures that show someone exercising.

Remember
A verb shows action.

run   eat   jump   ride   talk   throw

1. 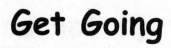 _____	2. _____	3. _____
4. _____	5. _____	6. _____

Directions What do you do to get exercise? Draw a picture. Write a paragraph to tell about it. Circle at least three verbs.

_____

_____

_____

_____

_____

The Ultimate Book of Second Grade Skills, SV 9781419099533
Verbs

Hear It for <u>Long o</u>

Directions Say each picture name. Write <u>o_e</u> to complete the word if you hear the **long o** sound.

Remember

bone | Long o can be spelled <u>o_e</u>.

1. r o p e	**2.** f x	**3.** c n
4. h s	**5.** t p	**6.** r b
7. c t	**8.** r s	**9.** m p
10. n s	**11.** p t	**12.** gl b

The Ultimate Book of Second Grade Skills, SV 9781419099533

Name _____ Date _____

On the Fact Trail

Remember
Look at the sign to see
if you add or subtract.

1. 34
  + 4
  ‾‾‾‾

5. 31
  − 20
  ‾‾‾‾

9. 77
  + 12
  ‾‾‾‾

13. 94
  − 30
  ‾‾‾‾

2. 49
  − 8
  ‾‾‾‾

6. 56
  + 33
  ‾‾‾‾

10. 20
  + 50
  ‾‾‾‾

14. 55
  + 32
  ‾‾‾‾

3. 26
  + 3
  ‾‾‾‾

7. 78
  − 67
  ‾‾‾‾

11. 69
  − 23
  ‾‾‾‾

15. 85
  − 75
  ‾‾‾‾

4. 45
  − 5
  ‾‾‾‾

8. 54
  + 44
  ‾‾‾‾

12. 98
  − 46
  ‾‾‾‾

16. 80
  + 13
  ‾‾‾‾

2-Digit Addition and Subtraction Without Regrouping
The Ultimate Book of Second Grade Skills, SV 9781419099533

Name _____ Date _____

Nouns and Verbs

Directions Read each word. Then write **noun** or **verb**.

Remember

A noun names a person, a place, or a thing. A verb shows action.

1. cup _____

2. gave _____

3. bring _____

4. milk _____

5. cat _____

6. say _____

7. kitchen _____

8. eat _____

9. write _____

10. see _____

Directions Use at least three nouns and three verbs from above to write about the picture.

_____

_____

_____

_____

_____

_____

_____

Name _____ Date _____

Go Slow for Long o

Read each clue. Write the letters on the buttons to make words with **long o** spelled **ow**.

Remember

Long o can be spelled ow.

bow

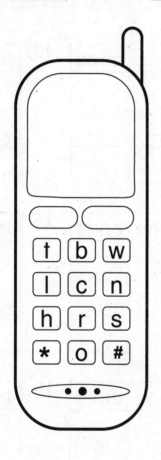

1. You can add this to a gift. ____ ____ ____

2. The wind does this. ____ ____ ____ ____

3. You can do this with a ball. ____ ____ ____ ____ ____

4. It is white and cold. ____ ____ ____ ____

5. It is black and can fly. ____ ____ ____ ____

6. It means not high. ____ ____ ____

Name _____   Date _____

Make a Ten

Directions Add.

Remember

Regroup by trading
10 ones for 1 ten.

1.

tens	ones
1	8
+	6

5.

tens	ones
3	4
+1	7

9.

tens	ones
1	6
+4	6

12.

tens	ones
7	3
+1	8

2.

tens	ones
2	3
+	9

6.

tens	ones
4	9
+2	9

10.

tens	ones
7	9
+1	7

13.

tens	ones
5	5
+2	6

3.

tens	ones
2	7
+1	3

7.

tens	ones
6	8
+2	5

11.

tens	ones
4	8
+3	9

14.

tens	ones
4	3
+3	7

4.

tens	ones
5	6
+2	9

8.

tens	ones
3	5
+	9

2-Digit Addition with Regrouping
The Ultimate Book of Second Grade Skills, SV 9781419099533

Be Exact

Directions Read each sentence. Write a more exact word for each <u>underlined</u> word. The first one has been done for you.

Remember
A good writer uses verbs that give a clear picture of the action.

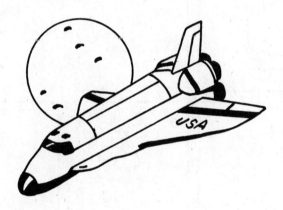

1. Spaceships <u>go</u> to the moon. _____ zoom _____

2. People <u>walk</u> to work. _____

3. Trains <u>move</u> along the tracks. _____

4. We <u>ride</u> our bicycles. _____

5. Fast cars <u>go</u> up the road. _____

6. The children <u>walk</u> in the hallways. _____

7. A man <u>runs</u> in the park. _____

8. A bus <u>goes</u> down the highway. _____

From Short to Long

Directions **Rewrite each word and add an _e_. Draw the picture that names the word.**

Remember

Long u has several spelling patterns.

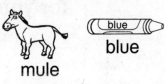

mule   blue

1. cub _____

2. cut _____

3. hug _____

4. tub _____

5. plum _____

Directions **Write a word from the box to complete each sentence.**

blue   due   glue

6. A story was _____ in school.

7. Tammy got some _____ paper to make a cover for it.

8. She used _____ to stick some shapes to it.

Name _____ Date _____

Race to Subtract

Directions Subtract.

Remember

Regroup by trading 1 ten for 10 ones.

1.

tens	ones
1	13
2	3
−	4

5.

tens	ones
5	3
− 1	8

9.

tens	ones
8	2
− 3	7

12.

tens	ones
9	5
− 5	6

2.

tens	ones
2	6
−	9

6.

tens	ones
3	7
− 2	9

10.

tens	ones
6	1
− 4	2

13.

tens	ones
5	5
−	7

3.

tens	ones
3	1
− 1	5

7.

tens	ones
6	3
− 2	9

11.

tens	ones
8	1
− 4	8

14.

tens	ones
7	0
− 6	7

4.

tens	ones
4	0
− 1	2

8.

tens	ones
4	4
−	5

2-Digit Subtraction with Regrouping
The Ultimate Book of Second Grade Skills, SV 9781419099533

Name _____   Date _____

Name That Story

Directions Read each selection. Write <u>fiction</u>, <u>nonfiction</u>, or <u>poem</u>.

1. An ostrich is a very large bird. Like all birds, an ostrich has feathers, a beak, and wings. Unlike other birds, the ostrich cannot fly. While most birds fly away from danger, the ostrich uses its eyes to see animals that are far away. Then it uses its long, strong legs to run away.

_____

2. I am sure that you have heard,
How special is the ostrich bird!
It cannot fly, nor sing a song,
But its legs are long and very strong.
When it sees danger, it will not stay.
The ostrich's legs help it run away.

_____

3. "I want to fly," said Oliver. "I am a bird, and all birds fly."

"Your wings are too little for such a big body," said Bluebird. "But you have other parts that make you special. Your big eyes have saved me from Lion several times. You were able to see him from far away. And when my wing was hurt, you carried me on your back. You were able to run really fast so that I could get to the doctor."

"I guess you are right," said Oliver. "I can do lots of things that other birds cannot do."

_____

Name _____ Date _____

A Long Review

Directions Say each picture name. Circle the letter that stands for the vowel sound.

1. a e i o u	2. a e i o u
3. a e i o u	4. a e i o u
5. a e i o u	6. a e i o u
7. a e i o u	8. a e i o u
9. a e i o u	10. a e i o u

Mouse Time Math

Directions Add or subtract.

> **Remember**
> Look at the sign to see if you add or subtract. Then decide if you need to trade tens or ones.

1. 24
   + 7

2. 38
   − 9

3. 45
   − 18

4. 59
   + 11

5. 62
   − 33

6. 56
   + 29

7. 84
   − 27

8. 77
   + 13

9. 53
   + 27

10. 80
    − 36

11. 61
    − 8

12. 25
    + 45

13. 74
    − 25

14. 66
    + 16

15. 88
    − 79

16. 37
    + 29

2-Digit Addition and Subtraction with Regrouping
The Ultimate Book of Second Grade Skills, SV 9781419099533

Name _____ Date _____

A Trip to the Beach

Directions Draw a line to match each subject with a predicate.

Subject	Predicate
1. Children	swim far out in the ocean water.
2. Pretty shells	fly above the water.
3. White seagulls	build sand castles on the beach.
4. The sand	wash up on the beach for us to find.
5. Many fish	sticks to our feet.

Directions Read each group of words. Write <u>subject</u> or <u>predicate</u> to tell what it is. Then use the words to write complete sentences.

crash   Jane   Boys

6. The ocean waves _____

_____

7. dig a big hole. _____

_____

8. reads under an umbrella. _____

_____

I'm Growing!

Directions Read the list of ways you change. Write the letter in the chart to show the kind of change.

a. shoes too small
b. can tie shoes
c. clothes too small
d. can read
e. puts away toys
f. sets the table
g. can write
h. baby teeth fall out
i. keeps room neat

Bodies Growing	Learning Things	Being Responsible

People Grow and Change
The Ultimate Book of Second Grade Skills, SV 9781419099533

Name _____ Date _____

Hard and Soft Sounds

Directions Look at the underlined letter in each word. Color the two pictures in each row whose names have the same sound.

1. <u>c</u>ent	cup	mi<u>c</u>e	la<u>c</u>e
2. <u>c</u>ap	<u>c</u>ity	<u>c</u>at	<u>c</u>ot
3. <u>g</u>oat	<u>g</u>um	ba<u>g</u>	<u>g</u>erbil
4. <u>gi</u>raffe	<u>g</u>ame	<u>g</u>iant	ca<u>g</u>e
5. <u>s</u>un	<u>s</u>ink	ho<u>s</u>e	<u>g</u>as
6. ro<u>s</u>e	<u>s</u>ock	chee<u>s</u>e	mu<u>s</u>ic
7. <u>s</u>ugar	ti<u>ss</u>ue	<u>s</u>eal	mi<u>ss</u>ion

Variant *c, g,* and *s*
The Ultimate Book of Second Grade Skills, SV 9781419099533

Name _____   Date _____

Bakery Buys

Directions Color the coins you need to buy each treat.

1.

2.

3.

4.

5.

Counting Coins
The Ultimate Book of Second Grade Skills, SV 9781419099533

Happy Endings

Directions Add <u>ing</u> to each word. Write the new word on the lines.

1. skip _____ _____ _____ _____ _____ _____ _____ _____
1

2. walk _____ _____ _____ _____ _____ _____ _____
2

3. play _____ _____ _____ _____ _____ _____ _____
3

4. talk _____ _____ _____ _____ _____ _____ _____
4

5. bike _____ _____ _____ _____ _____ _____
5

6. run _____ _____ _____ _____ _____ _____ _____
6

7. hug _____ _____ _____ _____ _____ _____ _____
7

Directions Write the numbered letters from above on the lines below.

Riddle:

What action is "wheel" fun?

_____ _____ _____ _____ _____ _____ _____
 1   2   3   4   5   6   7

Verbs Ending in *ing*
The Ultimate Book of Second Grade Skills, SV 9781419099533

Name _____   Date _____

Recycling Rules

Directions Read the paragraph. Then tell at least two ways to reduce, reuse, or recycle each thing.

Resources are things in nature that people use, like fish, rocks, and oil. Some resources are being used up. They cannot be replaced. People need to reduce, reuse, and recycle to help keep the resources safe. People use less of something when they reduce. They reuse something when they find a new use for it. People recycle when they take used goods and change them to make new, useful things.

1.

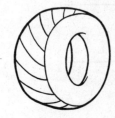

_____

_____

_____

2.

_____

_____

_____

3.

_____

_____

_____

The Ultimate Book of Second Grade Skills, SV 9781419099533

Name _____   Date _____

More Than Just <u>s</u>

Directions Say each picture name. Write a blend from the box to complete the words.

| sc   sk   sl   sn   sp   st   sw |

1. ____ ider	**2.** ____ ake	**3.** ____ unk
4. ____ ed	**5.** ____ ar	**6.** ____ arf
7. ____ ail	**8.** ____ oon	**9.** ____ ate
10. ____ amp	**11.** ____ ide	**12.** ____ im

Blends with *s*
The Ultimate Book of Second Grade Skills, SV 9781419099533

Name _____ Date _____

Big Numbers

Directions Write 100 less and 100 more.

1.  113   213   313

4.  ___   470   ___

2. ___   745   ___

5.  ___   186   ___

3. ___   494   ___

6. ___   899   ___

Remember

> means "is greater than."
< means "is less than."

Directions Write < or >.

7. 100 $<$ 200   **10.** 281 ◯ 291   **13.** 428 ◯ 248

8. 384 ◯ 383   **11.** 845 ◯ 945   **14.** 367 ◯ 365

9. 576 ◯ 567   **12.** 235 ◯ 352   **15.** 939 ◯ 940

Compare Numbers
The Ultimate Book of Second Grade Skills, SV 9781419099533

Tell It Like It Is

Directions Read each group of sentences. Then write numbers
<u>1</u> through <u>5</u> to show the story order.

Bath Time

_____ Next Jen gets the dog.

_____ First she gets out the tub and soap.

_____ Finally Jen rubs her dog until he is dry.

___1___ Jen decides to give her dog a bath.

_____ Then Jen washes her dog until he is clean.

A Butterfly

_____ Then it eats lots of leaves and grows
really big.

_____ A caterpillar can change into a butterfly.

_____ Finally the caterpillar breaks out of the
chrysalis as a butterfly.

_____ First the caterpillar hatches out of the egg.

_____ Next it becomes a chrysalis.

The Ultimate Book of Second Grade Skills, SV 9781419099533

Name _____   Date _____

Let's Stay Healthy

Directions Unscramble the underlined letters to complete the sentences that tell how to stay healthy.

1.    Use soap to <u>shaw</u> every day. _____

2.    Brush your <u>thete</u>. _____

3.    Eat healthy <u>odof</u>. _____

4.    Go to <u>deb</u> early. _____

5.    Use suntan <u>nolito</u> while out in the sun.

_____

Healthy Lifestyles
The Ultimate Book of Second Grade Skills, SV 9781419099533

Name _____   Date _____

"r" You Listening?

Directions Say each picture name. Write a blend from the box to complete the words.

br   cr   dr   fr   gr   pr   tr

1. _____ib	**2.** _____ush	**3.** _____ain
4. _____um	**5.** _____ill	**6.** _____uit
7. _____ayon	**8.** _____ead	**9.** _____uck
10. _____apes	**11.** _____ame	**12.** _____etzel

Weigh In

Directions Circle the best estimate.

1.	 3 ounces 3 pounds	**2.**	 8 ounces 8 pounds
3.	3 pounds 30 pounds	**4.**	 2 pounds 2,000 pounds
5.	 15 pounds 500 pounds	**6.**	 10 pounds 100 pounds
7.	 I pound I ton	**8.**	 I pound I ton

Weight
The Ultimate Book of Second Grade Skills, SV 9781419099533

Day by Day

Name _____ **Date** _____

Directions Write the name of each day correctly. Draw a line to match it to the abbreviation.

> **Remember**
> An abbreviation is a short way to write a word. It begins with a capital letter and ends with a period.

1. tuesday   _____   Mon.

2. sunday   _____   Thurs.

3. friday   _____   Sun.

4. wednesday _____   Sat.

5. monday   _____   Tues.

6. thursday   _____   Fri.

7. saturday   _____   Wed.

Directions Write the abbreviations for the days of the week in order on the weekly calendar. Write a schedule of activities you do.

_____	_____	_____	_____	_____	_____	_____

Days of the Week
The Ultimate Book of Second Grade Skills, SV 9781419099533

A Family Feeling

Directions Circle the letter of the sentence that tells about each picture.

I. **A.** Family members make fun of each other.

B. Family members help each other when someone is sad.

2. **A.** Family members show love.

B. Family members hurt one another's feelings.

3. **A.** Family members like to talk and laugh when they are together.

B. Family members get angry at each other when they are together.

Family Feelings
The Ultimate Book of Second Grade Skills, SV 9781419099533

Looking for l

Directions Say each picture name. Write a blend from the box to complete the words.

bl cl fl gl pl sl

1. _____ute	2. _____obe	3. _____ock
4. _____ue	5. _____own	6. _____y
7. _____ock	8. _____um	9. _____ug
10. _____ed	11. _____ack	12. _____ide

Blends with l
The Ultimate Book of Second Grade Skills, SV 9781419099533

Name _____   Date _____

Grid Fun

Directions Start at 0. Follow the directions. What shape is at that point? Draw the shape.

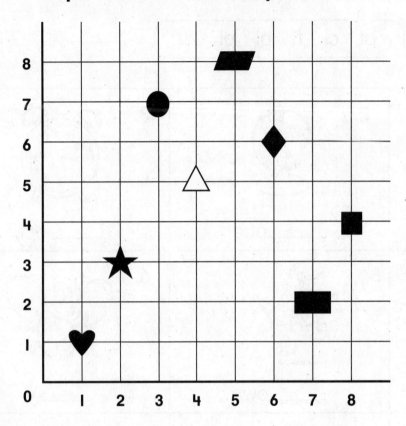

	Right	Up	Shape		Right	Up	Shape
1.	→ 2	↑ 3		5.	→ 7	↑ 2	
2.	→ 6	↑ 6		6.	→ 4	↑ 5	
3.	→ 1	↑ 1		7.	→ 8	↑ 4	
4.	→ 3	↑ 7		8.	→ 5	↑ 8	

Grid
The Ultimate Book of Second Grade Skills, SV 9781419099533

Art Start

Directions Circle the word that correctly completes the sentence.

> **Remember**
> Words that tell about something that happened in the past often end in ed.

1. Yesterday Tran (visits, visited) the art museum.

2. He (looks, looked) at many beautiful paintings.

3. He (watches, watched) an artist at work.

4. Tran (asks, asked) many questions about painting.

5. He (learns, learned) a lot.

6. Now Tran (paints, painted) every day.

7. He (wants, wanted) to take painting lessons soon.

8. He (hopes, hoped) to be a famous artist someday.

Name _____ Date _____

Sensing What's Around

1.

Which can you taste?

chair   ham   yard   corn

gum   flag   brush   bread

2.

Which can you smell?

rain   desk   grass   lamp

rose   star   soap   fork

3.

Which can you see?

bug   burn   book   rose

best   horse   grow   barn

4.

Which can you touch?

spring   bird   shirt   yarn

born   new   dirt   moon

5.

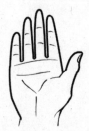

Which can you hear?

horn   harm   bark   smile

chirp   grass   purr   flute

Name _____ Date _____

A Good Ending

1.	2.	3.	4.
st nd sk	st nd nt	nd mp sp	mp st nt

5.	6.	7.	8.
sk sp st	mp nt sk	nt mp nd	sm mp nt

9.	10.	11.	12.
nk sk st	sk mt nt	mp nt nd	sp st sk

13.	14.	15.	16.
mp nt nd	st sp sk	sp st sk	sk nk nd

Final Blends
The Ultimate Book of Second Grade Skills, SV 9781419099533

Tools We Use

Name _____   Date _____

Directions Draw a line to match the **best** tool you would use to measure.

1.

```
1 2 3 4 5 6 7 8
```

2.

3.

4.

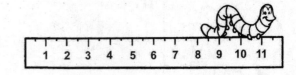

5.

6.

Measurement Tools
The Ultimate Book of Second Grade Skills, SV 9781419099533

Name _____ Date _____

Puzzled About Endings

Solve the puzzles to make words.

1. skate – e + ing ◯ ___ ___ ___ ___ ___

2. name – e + ed ___ ___ ◯ ___ ___

3. like – e + ing ___ ◯ ___ ___ ___ ___

4. close – e + ing ___ ◯ ___ ___ ___ ___ ___

5. sneeze – e + ed ___ ___ ◯ ___ ___ ___ ___

6. score – e + ed ___ ___ ___ ___ ◯

(Directions) **Write the letters from the circles above in order to solve the riddle.**

What did the cat do when it saw a mouse?

It ___ ___ ___ ___ ___ ___ .
    1   2   3   4   5   6

Verbs with Spelling Changes
The Ultimate Book of Second Grade Skills, SV 9781419099533

Name _____ Date _____

Your Neighborhood

Directions Look at the picture of a neighborhood. Think about your neighborhood. Write two sentences to tell how it is the same. Write two sentences to tell how it is different.

GREEN PARK

1. The neighborhoods are the same because _____

_____

_____

2. The neighborhoods are different because _____

_____

_____

Word Equations

Directions Use the clues in each box to find a new word. Write the word on the line.

1. wet − et + hen =

_____

2. ship − p + ne =

_____

3. the − e + in =

_____

4. chin − n + ck =

_____

5. is + hop − i =

_____

6. whip − ip + eel =

_____

Directions Make up your own puzzles. Start with one of the words in the box.

shine thing show champ

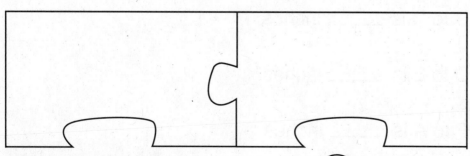

101

Initial Consonant Digraphs
The Ultimate Book of Second Grade Skills, SV 9781419099533

The Busy Bee

Directions Look at the path of the bee. Use an inch ruler to measure the distance between the flowers.

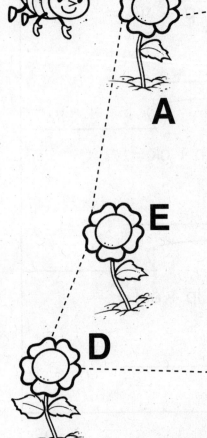

A

B

E

D

C

1. The distance from A to B is _____ inches.

2. The distance from B to C is _____ inches.

3. The distance from C to D is _____ inches.

4. The distance from D to E is _____ inches.

5. The distance from E to A is _____ inches.

Inches
The Ultimate Book of Second Grade Skills, SV 9781419099533

Name _____ Date _____

Sentence Sense

Directions Read each sentence. Write <u>S</u> if it is a statement.
Write <u>Q</u> if it is a question.

Remember

A statement is a sentence that tells something. A question is a sentence that asks something. A statement ends in a period (.). A question ends in a question mark (?). Both kinds of sentences begin with a capital letter.

---

1. Where did Maria go? _____

2. Maria went to the zoo. _____

3. Maria wanted to see the new wildlife area. _____

4. What time will Maria be back? _____

5. She will be back in an hour. _____

Directions Read each group of words. Is it a statement or a question? Write the words correctly.

6. what will Maria do when she gets back

_____

7. she will go to her drum lesson

_____

8. Maria wants to play in a band someday

_____

Name _____ Date _____

That Old Feeling

_____

Directions Write a word from the box to name each feeling.
Tell about a time when you had that feeling.

┌───┐
  happy   mad   surprised   worried
└───┘

1.  _____

   _____

   _____

2.  _____

   _____

   _____

3.  _____

   _____

   _____

4.  _____

   _____

   _____

Emotions
The Ultimate Book of Second Grade Skills, SV 9781419099533

It's the Law

Directions Unscramble the underlined letters to tell about laws.
Write the words on the lines.

1. A <u>alw</u> is a community rule. _____

2. Laws keep people in a community <u>esaf</u>. _____

3. Laws also keep a community <u>necal</u>. _____

4. Laws are <u>raif</u> to everyone. _____

Directions Look at each picture. Write a sentence to tell the law.

5. _____

_____

_____

_____

6. _____

_____

_____

_____

Make a List

Directions Write a word from the box to name each picture.

wrist	knight	wrench	sign	knee
gnome	knife	write	gnaw	

1. 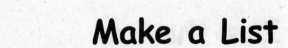	2.	3.
_____	_____	_____

4.	5.	6. STOP
_____	_____	_____

7.	8.	9.
_____	_____	_____

Directions Write the words in the column to tell the sound of <u>kn</u>, <u>wr</u>, and <u>gn</u>.

10. <u>n</u> sound spelled k<u>n</u>   **11.** <u>n</u> sound spelled g<u>n</u>   **12.** <u>r</u> sound spelled w<u>r</u>

_____   _____   _____

_____   _____   _____

_____   _____   _____

Name _____   Date _____

Bugged by Length

Directions Read to find out how far each ladybug crawls. Then use an inch ruler to draw a line to show the length.

1.

● 3 inches

_____

2.

● 1 inch

_____

3.

● 6 inches

_____

4.

● 2 inches

_____

5.

● 4 inches

Inches
The Ultimate Book of Second Grade Skills, SV 9781419099533

Name _____ Date _____

Tell It Like It Is

Directions Look at the picture. Write an adjective to complete each sentence.

1. It was a _____ summer day.

2. Carla ate some _____ ice cream.

3. Her cone had _____ scoops.

4. It was so _____ that the ice cream began to melt.

5. A _____ dog liked the drops.

6. Carla and the dog both enjoyed the _____ treat.

Name _____   Date _____

Seasons in a Year

Directions Write the name of a season to complete each
sentence. Then answer the question.

winter   spring   summer   fall

1. In _____, we like to swim.

2. In _____, leaves on the trees turn bright colors.

3. In _____, we wear coats to stay warm.

4. In _____, flowers begin to grow.

What is your favorite season? _____

Directions Draw a picture to show what you like to do during
your favorite season.

Seasons
The Ultimate Book of Second Grade Skills, SV 9781419099533

Name _____ Date _____

Sign Me Up!

Directions Signs tell about rules and laws. What does each sign below tell you?

1.  _____
   _____

2.  _____
   _____

3.  _____
   _____

4.  _____
   _____

Directions What sign is in your neighborhood? Draw it. Write a sentence to tell what it means.

_____
_____
_____

Vowels with r

Directions Write a word from the box that names each picture.

car   fork   horse   park   porch   yarn

1.

◯ ◯ ___ ___ ___ ___ ___

4.

◯ ___ ___ ___ ___ ___

2.

◯ ___ ___ ___ ___

5.

◯ ___ ___ ___ ___

3.

◯ ___ ___ ___

6.

___ ___ ___ ◯ ___

Directions Write the circled letters above in order to answer the riddle.

What did the baby corn call its father?

___ ___ ___ ___ ___ ___ ___

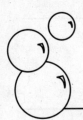

At a Snail's Pace

Directions Use a centimeter ruler to measure how far each snail crawls.

1.

_____ cm

2.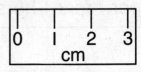

_____ cm

3.

_____ cm

4.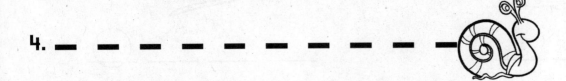

_____ cm

5.

_____ cm

Centimeters
The Ultimate Book of Second Grade Skills, SV 9781419099533

Name _____ Date _____

Hello, Mister Bird!

Directions Write rhyming words from the box to complete the poem.

me	red	said	head
see	tree	fled	happily

1. When I was sitting under a _____,

2. I heard a bird chirp _____.

3. I looked up high and what did I _____,

4. But a beautiful bird sitting above _____!

5. Its wings and chest were colored _____.

6. It had a crest upon its _____.

7. "Hello, Mister Bird!" I _____.

8. It quickly spread its wings and _____.

Name _____ Date _____

Down It Goes

Directions Draw lines to match each body part to what it does.

Body Part	What It Does
1. mouth	chews the food
2. stomach	takes food into the body
3. tongue	crushes food and turns it into a thick liquid
4. teeth	tastes food and pushes it into the throat

Directions Use the body parts from above to label the diagram.

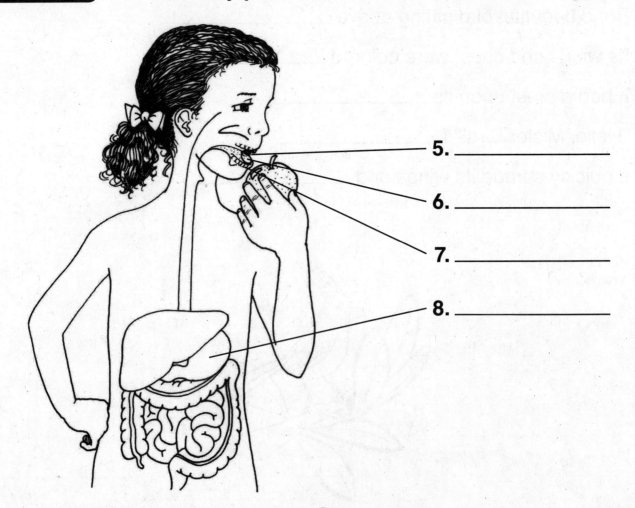

5. _____

6. _____

7. _____

8. _____

Digestion
The Ultimate Book of Second Grade Skills, SV 9781419099533

Follow Rules

Directions Draw a line from each picture to the rule it shows.

1.

Wear a helmet when riding a bike.

2.

Take turns when playing games.

3.

Wait your turn in line without playing.

Directions Circle the child above who is not following a rule.
Tell why it is important to follow this rule.

_____

_____

_____

The Ultimate Book of Second Grade Skills, SV 9781419099533

Name _____ Date _____

Tricky Vowels

Directions Say each word in the box. Then write the word under the picture that has the same vowel sound.

beach	bead	head	heavy
pea	seat	spread	thread

Remember

The vowel spelling ea can stand for two sounds.

leaf   bread

1.

_____

_____

_____

_____

2.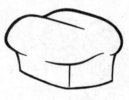

_____

_____

_____

_____

Directions Use a word from above to complete each sentence.

3. Fran went to the _____.

4. She carried a big, _____ bag filled with the things she would need.

5. Fran _____ a blanket on the sand.

6. Then she took a _____ on the blanket.

7. Finally Fran put a hat on her _____.

Name _____   Date _____

Shape Up

Directions **Read each riddle about a shape.
Then draw the shape.**

1. I have four sides and four corners.
All my sides are the same length.
What shape am I?

_____

2. I have four sides and four corners.
The opposite sides are the same length.
What shape am I?

_____

3. I have no sides and no corners.
I am round.
What shape am I?

_____

4. I have three sides and three corners.
My sides can be different lengths.
What shape am I?

Name _____ Date _____

A Capital Idea

Directions Underline the words that are proper nouns. Cross out each letter that should be a capital letter. Write a capital letter above it.

Remember

A proper noun names a specific person, place, or thing. A proper noun begins with a capital letter.

1. Lana is in north carolina.

2. She is visiting her grandmother in raleigh.

3. Lana's grandmother is jan washington.

4. Mrs. Washington lives on oak street.

5. Lana and her grandmother went to the north carolina zoo.

6. Lana will return to topeka, kansas, on Tuesday.

7. She will be happy to get back to her house on park street.

8. She knows hill elementary school will start in one week.

9. School will start on september I.

10. Lana and her brother lee will shop for school supplies.

Proper Nouns
The Ultimate Book of Second Grade Skills, SV 9781419099533

Name _____   Date _____

Take Time for Teeth

Directions Look at the color code. Color the tooth to label the diagram. Then answer the questions.

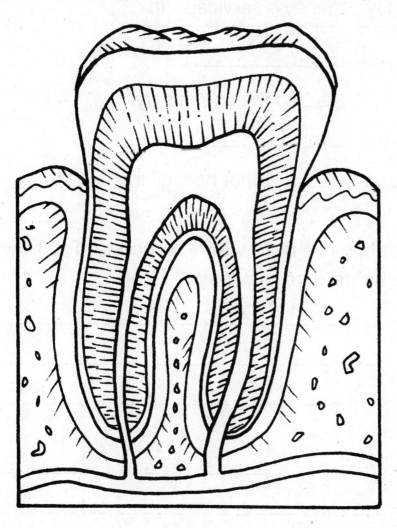

roots	=	blue
gum	=	red
pulp	=	green
dentin	=	yellow
enamel	=	purple

1. What part of the tooth can you see? _____

2. What part of your mouth helps hold the tooth to the bone?

   _____

3. Which part of a tooth is yellow and harder than bone?

   _____

Tooth Parts
The Ultimate Book of Second Grade Skills, SV 9781419099533

Name _____ Date _____

Your Taxes at Work

Directions Write a word from the box to complete each sentence.

> community   money   services   tax

1. Many people live together in a _____.

2. The people give _____ to the community.

3. The money paid is called a _____.

4. The money pays for _____ that help all the people.

Directions The people below are paid with tax money. Tell how each person helps a community.

5.  _____

_____

_____

6. 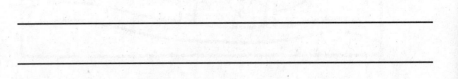 _____

_____

_____

7.  _____

_____

Taxes
The Ultimate Book of Second Grade Skills, SV 9781419099533

Name _____ Date _____

Give It the Boot

Directions Say each word in the box. Then write the word under the picture that has the same vowel sound.

Remember

The vowel spelling <u>oo</u> can stand for two sounds.

foot   boot

book	cook	good	goose	look
moon	room	stood	tool	zoo

1.

_____

_____

_____

2.

_____

_____

_____

Directions Use a word from above to complete each sentence.

3. Pam was sitting in her _____.

4. She was reading a _____.

5. It was about a cat and mouse who flew to the _____.

6. They wanted to _____ at it to find out if it was made of cheese.

7. Pam thought is was a very _____ book.

Vowel Digraph *oo*
The Ultimate Book of Second Grade Skills, SV 9781419099533

Name _____ Date _____

Shaped for Fun

Directions Look at the shapes at the beginning of each row. Circle the name of the shape they make when joined together. Then draw the shape.

1.
   circle   rectangle   square

2.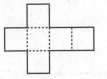
   circle   rectangle   square

3.
   circle   rectangle   square

Directions Look at the shape at the beginning of each row. Circle the name of the figure it makes when folded. Then draw the shape.

4.
   cube   cylinder   pyramid

5.
   cube   cylinder   pyramid

6.
   cube   cylinder   pyramid

Shapes
The Ultimate Book of Second Grade Skills, SV 9781419099533

Name _____   Date _____

Time for Temperature

Directions Circle the best estimate.

1.	90°F 60°F	2.	50°F 30°F
3.	70°F 40°F	4.	80°F 50°F
5.	80°F 60°F	6.	80°F 50°F

Directions Write the temperature.

7. °F
20°
10°
0°

_____ °F

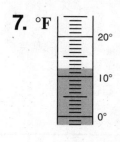

8. °F
100°
90°
80°

_____ °F

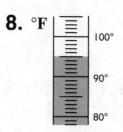

9. °F
40°
30°
20°

_____ °F

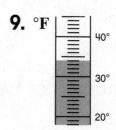

10. °F
80°
70°
60°

_____ °F

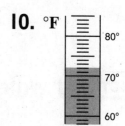

Temperature
The Ultimate Book of Second Grade Skills, SV 9781419099533

Name _____ Date _____

Snacking Advice

Directions Say each picture name. Write the letter of the first sound to learn about eating snacks.

1.

_____ _____ _____ _____ _____ _____

2.

_____ _____ _____ _____ _____ _____ _____

3.

_____ _____ _____ _____ _____ _____

Directions Write the names of two healthy snacks you eat.

_____

_____

Healthy Foods
The Ultimate Book of Second Grade Skills, SV 9781419099533

In the Lead

Directions Use the words in the box to complete the puzzle.
Then answer the question.

governor   leaders   mayor   president   vote

Across

4. People who make the rules in the community

5. The leader of the United States

Down

1. The way people choose leaders

2. The leader of a state

3. The leader of a city

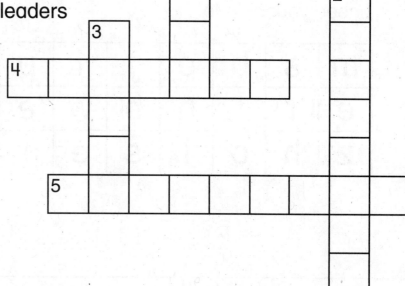

6. Why is it important to have good leaders? Give two reasons.

_____

_____

_____

Leaders
The Ultimate Book of Second Grade Skills, SV 9781419099533

Help the Chief

Directions Decode the message to find out how to help Chief Shield. Color the letter in the first box. Skip the second box. Keep using this pattern to color a box and then skip a box.

Dear Tommie,
I need your help to

m	s	b	e	j	i	p	z	k
e	r	t	h	h	w	e	l	t
z	h	o	i	s	e	m	f	n

Chief Shield

What will Tommie do? Write the letters that are not colored in order.

_____ _____ _____ _____ _____

_____ _____

Fraction Action

Directions Circle the two shapes in each row that show the fraction.

1. $\frac{1}{2}$			
2. $\frac{1}{3}$		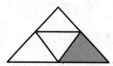	
3. $\frac{1}{4}$			

Directions What part is shaded? Circle the fraction.

4.

$\frac{1}{2}$ $\frac{1}{3}$ $\frac{1}{4}$

6.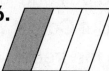

$\frac{2}{3}$ $\frac{3}{3}$ $\frac{1}{3}$

8.

$\frac{1}{4}$ $\frac{2}{4}$ $\frac{3}{4}$

10.

$\frac{1}{3}$ $\frac{2}{3}$ $\frac{3}{3}$

5.

$\frac{1}{3}$ $\frac{2}{3}$ $\frac{2}{2}$

7.

$\frac{1}{2}$ $\frac{2}{2}$ $\frac{3}{4}$

9.

$\frac{1}{3}$ $\frac{3}{3}$ $\frac{3}{4}$

Fractions
The Ultimate Book of Second Grade Skills, SV 9781419099533

A Reason for Writing

Directions Read each story. Then darken the circle for the sentence that tells why the author wrote the story.

1. A quilt is a blanket made of different pieces of cloth. Many people have quilts on their beds. The quilts keep them warm in the cold weather. A long time ago, quilts had other uses, too. The people could not get paint and paper. But they had lots of old clothes. They cut squares of fabric from the clothes. They sewed them together to make colorful patterns and pictures. Quilts are now a popular kind of art.

○ **A.** The author wanted to tell a funny story about quilts.

○ **B.** The author wanted to get people to sew quilts.

○ **C.** The author wanted to tell how people use quilts.

2. Sam took his dog Comet for a walk. Along the way, Comet saw a squirrel. Comet began to pull and jump. Sam tried hard to hold on to his dog. But Comet was too strong. Comet pulled Sam around the trees, over the bushes, and into the water. Finally the squirrel disappeared into some rocks.

Sam sat down. Comet sat beside him, his tongue hanging out. He gave Sam a big lick.

Sam laughed, "I can't be mad at you! I got some good exercise."

○ **A.** The author wanted to tell people to train their dogs to behave.

○ **B.** The author wanted to tell a funny story about a dog.

○ **C.** The author wanted to give facts about dogs.

Name _____ Date _____

Out with Friends

Directions Imagine you are eating in a restaurant with friends. What will you order? Write your choices below.

MENU

Meats		**Fruits**		**Drinks**	
Hamburger	$1.25	Apple	$0.50	Soda	$1.00
Hot Dog	$1.00	Orange	$0.50	Milk	$0.50
Fried Chicken	$2.00	Banana	$0.50	Tea	$0.50
Pizza	$1.75	Strawberries	$1.00	Water	Free

Vegetables		**Desserts**	
Salad	$1.00	Chocolate Cake	$1.50
Peas	$0.50	Peanut Butter Cookies	$0.75
Green Beans	$0.50	Banana Pudding	$1.00
Carrots	$0.50	Ice Cream	$1.00

Order: _____

_____

Directions Did you order a healthy meal? Explain.

_____

_____

_____

_____

Healthy Foods
The Ultimate Book of Second Grade Skills, SV 9781419099533

Name _____   Date _____

Earth-Friendly Words

Directions Read the words in the box. Then unscramble the words to make the words in the box. Write a sentence using one of the words.

Earth	ecology	erosion	garbage
litter	pollution	recycle	trash

1. onioser _____

2. sthar _____

3. raEht _____

4. tetirl _____

5. ycologe _____

6. grabaeg _____

7. otniulplo _____

8. ecycerl _____

_____

_____

Resources
The Ultimate Book of Second Grade Skills, SV 9781419099533

A Long a Puzzle

Directions Read each clue. Write **long a** words spelled with the pattern **eigh** to complete the puzzle

Across

1. What can you ride in the snow?

3. What word means how heavy a thing is?

5. How many legs does a spider have?

6. What does a horse say?

Down

2. What number comes after seventeen?

4. What do you call someone who lives next door?

Name _____ Date _____

Colored Shapes

Directions Color each shape to show the fraction.

1.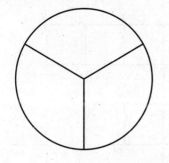

$\dfrac{2}{3}$

2.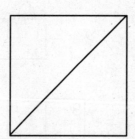

$\dfrac{1}{2}$

3.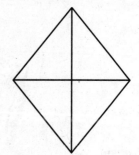

$\dfrac{3}{4}$

4.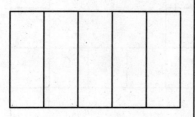

$\dfrac{2}{5}$

5.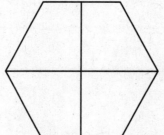

$\dfrac{3}{4}$

6.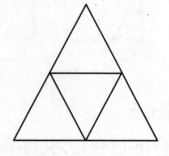

$\dfrac{2}{4}$

7.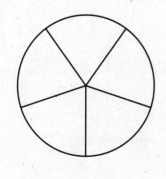

$\dfrac{4}{5}$

8.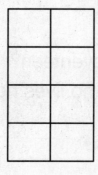

$\dfrac{6}{8}$

9.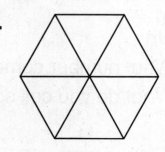

$\dfrac{5}{6}$

Name _____ Date _____

Let's Compare

Directions Write words to tell about the pictures in each row.

> **Remember**
>
> An adjective is a word that describes something. Add er to most adjectives to compare two persons, places, or things. Add est to most adjectives to compare three or more persons, places, or things.

1. young

younger

youngest

_____ _____ _____

2. long

longer

longest

_____ _____ _____

3. big

bigger

biggest

_____ _____ _____

4. tall

taller

tallest

_____ _____ _____

Adjectives
The Ultimate Book of Second Grade Skills, SV 9781419099533

Name _____ Date _____

Enjoying Exercise

Directions Write words from the box to name each kind of exercise. Then answer the question.

jump   skate   swim   run   dance   pedal

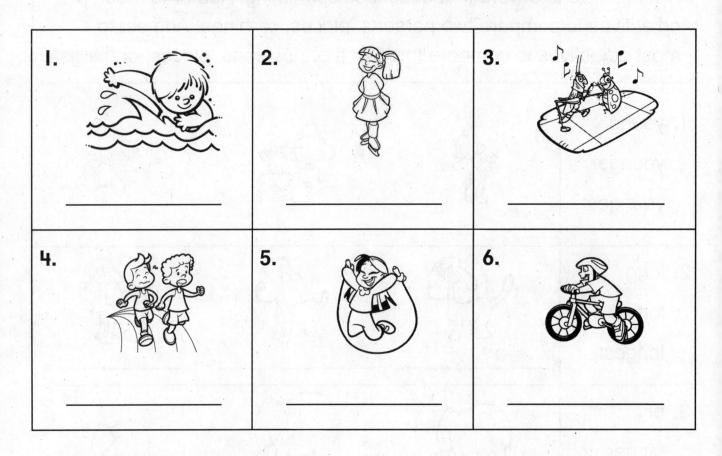

1. _____

2. _____

3. _____

4. _____

5. _____

6. _____

7. Why should you exercise?

_____

_____

_____

Exercise
The Ultimate Book of Second Grade Skills, SV 9781419099533

Name _____ Date _____

Awesome Sounding Words

Directions Read the clues. Then use the code to write the words with the correct spelling pattern.

Remember

The vowel pairs au and aw can sound the same.

sauce   paw

---

th____ ____   h____ ____k   p____ ____se   str____ ____

f____ ____n   h____ ____l   cl____ ____   t____ ____ght

Directions Write a word from the box to answer the clues.

1. A large bird _____

2. To stop for a bit _____

3. To melt _____

4. A baby deer _____

5. An animal's nail _____

6. To move or pull _____

7. Helped to learn _____

8. Dried grass _____

Vowels *au* and *aw*
The Ultimate Book of Second Grade Skills, SV 9781419099533

Name _____ Date _____

Pizza Party

Directions Cut each pizza so that everyone gets an equal part.

1.

2.

3.

4.

Fractions
The Ultimate Book of Second Grade Skills, SV 9781419099533

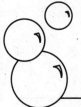

Pausing for Commas

Directions Read each sentence. Write a comma (,) where it is needed.

> **Remember**
> Use commas to separate three or more items listed in a sentence.

1. Rita Jess and Tom went for a walk.

2. They put on coats scarves and mittens.

3. The friends saw a squirrel deer and raccoon along the way.

4. The leaves were turning red orange and yellow.

5. The hikers were tired cold and hungry when they got back home.

6. Rita fixed hot chocolate cookies and crackers to eat.

7. Rita asked, "Do you want to play games sing songs or watch TV?"

8. Rita Jess and Tom decided to do all three.

Name _____ Date _____

Safe with Animals

Directions Draw a line to match a picture to the rule the child is breaking.

Rules

1.

A. Never touch a wild animal.

2.

B. Don't make loud noises around an animal.

3.

C. Never tease an animal.

4.

D. Never bother an animal when it is eating.

Directions Write another safety rule to follow when you are around animals.

_____

_____

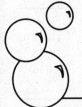

Getting Information

Directions Write the letter to tell where the information can be found. Sometimes, the information can be found in more than one place.

A.  B.  C.  D.

1. _____ Mark wants to find out who won the game last night.

2. _____ Liz wants to find out where a river is located.

3. _____ Mr. Roberts want to see what time a movie is showing.

4. _____ Jill wants to know about the animals living in Africa.

5. _____ Lisa wants to buy a pet puppy.

6. _____ Juan wants to know if he should wear a raincoat tomorrow.

7. _____ Mei wants to know what time her mother's flight will arrive.

8. _____ Kate wants to know when a train leaves.

Name _____   Date _____

Vowel Sounds of <u>ou</u> and <u>ow</u>

Directions Read the words in the puzzle.
Color the words brown that have
the same vowel sound as <u>house</u>
and <u>clown</u>. Color all other pieces
yellow. Then write a word in brown
to complete each sentence.

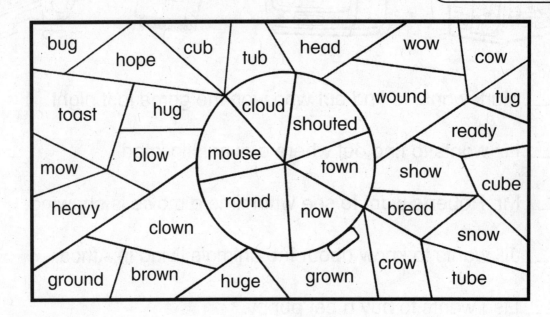

1. Ben saw something on the gr_____ _____nd.

2. It had a r_____ _____nd face.

3. It had a br_____ _____n band.

4. Ben picked it up and w_____ _____nd it.

5. "W_____ _____!" he sh_____ _____ted.

Directions What did Ben find? Write the answer below.

_____

Name _____ Date _____

Stuck on Gum

Directions Color the gum balls. Then answer the questions.

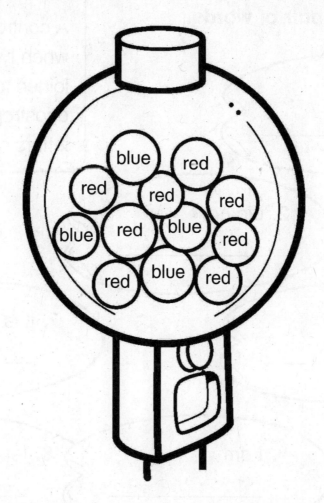

1. Which color of gum ball are you more likely to get? Why?

_____

_____

2. Which color of gum ball are you less likely to get? Why?

_____

_____

Probability
The Ultimate Book of Second Grade Skills, SV 9781419099533

Leaping Lily Pads

Directions Write the contraction for each pair of words.

Remember
A contraction is made when two words are joined together. An apostrophe shows where letters are missing.

1. was not

_____

2. did not

_____

3. we are

_____

7. it is

_____

4. I am

_____

8. let us

_____

5. have not

_____

6. do not

_____

Contractions
The Ultimate Book of Second Grade Skills, SV 9781419099533

Name _____   Date _____

Where Animals Live

Directions Draw a line to match each animal to the place it lives.

1.

A.

2.

B.

3.

C.

4.

D.

5.

E.

Animals and Regions
The Ultimate Book of Second Grade Skills, SV 9781419099533

How We Help

Directions Think about each person's job. Write <u>goods</u>, <u>services</u>, or <u>both</u> to tell what the person gives.

1. police officer	2. carpenter	3. farmer
_____	_____	_____
4. fisher	5. baker	6. mail carrier
_____	_____	_____

Name _____ Date _____

Tell All About It

Directions Read the words in the box. Use at least two words
to tell about each picture. Circle the words in the
sentences that have the same vowel sound as <u>book</u>
or <u>could</u>.

book	brook	cook	could	good
hood	look	stood	should	woods

1.

_____

_____

_____

2.

_____

_____

_____

3.

_____

_____

_____

145 *Vowels oo and ou*
The Ultimate Book of Second Grade Skills, SV 9781419099533

Name _____ Date _____

All the Way Around

Directions Use a centimeter ruler to find the perimeter around the shapes.

Remember
The perimeter is the distance around something.

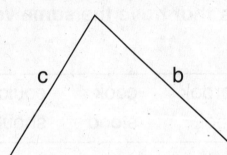

1. side a = _____ cm

2. side b = _____ cm

3. side c = _____ cm

4. (a) _____ + (b) _____ + (c) _____ = _____ cm

5. The perimeter of the triangle is _____.

6. side a = _____ cm

7. side b = _____ cm

8. side c = _____ cm

9. side d = _____ cm

10. (a) _____ + (b) _____ + (c) _____ + (d) _____ = _____ cm

11. The perimeter of the rectangle is _____.

Name _____ Date _____

One Rainy Day

(Directions) **Read the story. Then answer the questions.**

Kim looked out the window at the rain. She was very unhappy. She and her friend Maria had planned to take a picnic to the park today. Now they could not have a picnic because of the bad weather.

As Kim looked out the window, she saw Maria run across the yard. Maria had a big box in her hands. "What does Maria have?" wondered Kim. Kim raced to the door to let her friend in.

"I am so sad," said Kim. "We cannot have our picnic today."

"Oh, yes we can!" answered Maria. Then she opened the box. Kim saw sandwiches, fruit, and cookies. There was even a blanket to sit on.

"The rain is not going to change our plans," Maria said. "We are going to have a carpet picnic." Kim smiled and helped her friend spread out the blanket and food.

I. Why couldn't Kim and Maria take a picnic to the park?

_____

2. What was in Maria's box?

_____

3. How do you think Kim felt at the end of the story? How do you know?

_____

_____

Name _____ Date _____

A Home to Live

Directions Draw a line to match each animal to its home.

1.

A.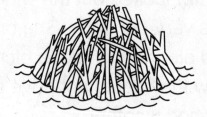

2.

B.

3.

C.

4.

D.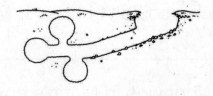

5.

E.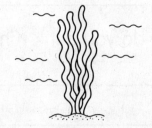

Animals and Homes
The Ultimate Book of Second Grade Skills, SV 9781419099533

Name _____ Date _____

Where Does Money Go?

Directions Use the grid to answer the questions. The first one is done for you.

	A	B	C	D
1	s	a	m	d
2	i	b	c	t
3	g	n	g	o
4	v	u	e	x

1. The money people make by working

   i   n   c   o   m   e
   A2 B3 C2 D3 C1 C4

2. A plan for spending money

   ___ ___ ___ ___ ___ ___
   B2 B4 D1 C3 C4 D2

3. Money that is put away and not spent

   ___ ___ ___ ___ ___ ___ ___
   A1 B1 A4 A2 B3 C3 A1

4. Money given to the government to pay for services

   ___ ___ ___ ___ ___
   D2 B1 D4 C4 A1

Directions Mr. Rios is making a budget. Circle the items that he **must** pay using his income.

apartment rent   water
food   gas
electricity   hat
dinner out   taxes
movie tickets

The Ultimate Book of Second Grade Skills, SV 9781419099533

Name _____   Date _____

Words with <u>r</u>

Directions Look at the pictures. Write words from the box to complete the puzzle.

bird   fern   herd   nurse   purse   shirt

1.

2.

3.

4.

5.

6.

Name _____ Date _____

Going Up

Directions **Add.**

Remember

First add the ones. Then add the tens. Finally add the hundreds.
Remember to regroup ones and tens if you need to.

---

1. 107
    +   5

2. 141
    +   9

3. 206
    +   5

4. 345
    +   7

5. 237
    + 25

6. 443
    + 62

7. 632
    + 79

8. 845
    + 98

9. 730
    + 247

10. 483
    + 317

11. 285
    + 290

12. 562
    + 348

13. 227
    + 135

14. 356
    + 279

15. 666
    + 141

16. 714
    + 116

Name _____ Date _____

All Year Long

Directions Write the months of the year correctly.

Remember
The names of the months begin with a capital letter. The abbreviations of the months begin with a capital letter and end with a period.

1. january _____

2. february _____

3. march _____

4. april _____

5. may _____

6. june _____

7. july _____

8. august _____

9. september _____

10. october _____

11. november _____

12. december _____

Directions Write the abbreviations of the months correctly.

13. jan _____   16. mar _____   19. nov _____

14. aug _____   17. sept _____   20. feb _____

15. oct _____   18. dec _____   21. apr _____

Months
The Ultimate Book of Second Grade Skills, SV 9781419099533

Winter Is Coming

Directions Write each animal name in the column to tell how it gets ready for winter.

snake	wolf	bat	rabbit
butterfly	raccoon	reindeer	groundhog
goose	worm	fox	bear

I.   I Sleep

2.   I Change

3.   I Move

_____

_____

_____

_____

Animal Characteristics
The Ultimate Book of Second Grade Skills, SV 9781419099533

Name _____   Date _____

Needs and Wants

Directions Write three things you need and one thing you want
in each category.

1. School	**2.** Activity
Need	Need
_____	_____
_____	_____
_____	_____
Want	Want
_____	_____
3. Clothes	**4.** Food
Need	Need
_____	_____
_____	_____
_____	_____
Want	Want
_____	_____

Needs and Wants
The Ultimate Book of Second Grade Skills, SV 9781419099533

Name _____ Date _____

Clue Me In!

Directions Write a word from the box to answer each clue.

blue	crew	drew	due
flew	glue	new	stew

1. What did the birds do? _____

2. Why is Tim's bike so shiny? _____

3. What did Mom make for dinner? _____

4. What did Dad use to fix the crack? _____

5. Where did Stan get that picture of a race car? _____

6. What color is the sky? _____

7. When do you return a library book? _____

8. What do you call the sailors on a ship? _____

Name _____   Date _____

Look at the Difference!

Directions Subtract.

> **Remember**
> First subtract the ones. Then subtract the tens. Finally subtract the hundreds. Remember to regroup hundreds, tens, and ones if you need to.

1. 135
    − 6

5. 428
    − 26

9. 600
    − 145

13. 342
     − 127

2. 196
    − 8

6. 503
    − 12

10. 729
     − 369

14. 482
     − 273

3. 274
    − 7

7. 761
    − 31

11. 537
     − 478

15. 751
     − 384

4. 362
    − 3

8. 855
    − 60

12. 931
     − 216

16. 900
     − 568

156
3-Digit Subtraction
The Ultimate Book of Second Grade Skills, SV 9781419099533

Make It a Capital

Directions Read the story. Circle the words that should be capitalized. Write the correct words under the columns.

It was saturday. Cora had just left spring mall on shady street. She was on her way to visit her best friend ryan. Ryan had gotten a new game from mrs. barton for his birthday last tuesday. The friends had not been able to play the game yet. The two had also

talked about going to rex art museum. The museum was showing some new paintings until the end of june. Cora liked art and did not want to miss the show. She hoped that ryan would go with her.

People	Places	Things
_____	_____	_____
_____	_____	_____
_____	_____	_____

Name _____ Date _____

A Frog's Life

Directions Write numbers $\underline{1}$ to $\underline{4}$ to show the order of a frog's life cycle. Then write words from the box to label the stage in the cycle.

tadpole   eggs   frog   tadpole with legs

_____	_____
_____	_____

Name _____ Date _____

Take or Make

Directions Look at each picture. Write **C** if the picture shows a consumer. Write **P** if the picture shows a producer.

Remember

A consumer takes and uses something. A producer makes something.

1.

_____

2.

_____

3.

_____

4.

_____

5.

_____

6.

_____

7.

_____

8.

_____

9.

_____

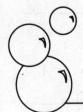

Name _____   Date _____

From the Beginning

Directions Write words from the box to complete the puzzle.

Remember

A prefix is a small word part added to the beginning of a root word that changes the meaning of the word.

retie	reread	unfair	unclear
reuse	unable	rewrite	unhappy

Across

2. Not able
3. Not happy
5. Write again
7. Read again

Down

1. Not fair
3. Not clear
4. Use again
6. Tie again

Directions Complete the sentences.

8. The prefix re means _____.

9. The prefix un means _____.

The Ultimate Book of Second Grade Skills, SV 9781419099533

Name _____   Date _____

A Masterpiece of Numbers

Directions Add or subtract.

Remember

Look at the sign. Then decide if you need to regroup hundreds, tens, or ones.

1. 104
    + 52

5. 219
    − 115

9. 800
    − 603

13. 720
    + 185

2. 263
    − 80

6. 632
    − 240

10. 553
    + 278

14. 549
    + 256

3. 371
    − 7

7. 475
    + 25

11. 627
    − 396

15. 862
    − 355

4. 489
    + 84

8. 391
    − 287

12. 754
    + 18

16. 643
    + 257

3-Digit Addition and Subtraction
The Ultimate Book of Second Grade Skills, SV 9781419099533

Name _____ Date _____

What a Character!

Directions Circle the picture that shows how the character is feeling in each story.

Remember
A character is a person, animal, or thing that the story is about.

1. Today was Keisha's birthday. No one had remembered. Her mother and father did not say anything at breakfast. Keisha's older sister left early. She did not give Keisha a hug. Keisha went to her room and sat on her bed. There was a big frown on her face.

2. Mr. Nixon watched his daughter walk out of the kitchen. Keisha looked so sad. But Mr. Nixon wanted to surprise Keisha. He had planned a big party. All of Keisha's friends were coming over. But Mr. Nixon was thinking. How would he get Keisha out of the house? He had to think of something so that Keisha would not know that she was going to have a surprise party.

3. Keisha rode her bike into the garage. She was upset that her father had asked her to go the store. What she thought was going to be a great day was not much fun.

Keisha grabbed the milk and walked in the front door.

"Surprise!" yelled everyone.

Keisha was surprised. All of her friends were there!

Story Characters
The Ultimate Book of Second Grade Skills, SV 9781419099533

Name _____   Date _____

At the Zoo

Directions   Look at the zoo homes. Which animals could live in each place? Write the names of at least three animals for each.

Animal Characteristics
The Ultimate Book of Second Grade Skills, SV 9781419099533

Big Changes

Directions Look at each picture. Write three ways people changed the land.

1.

_____

_____

_____

_____

_____

_____

_____

2.

_____

_____

_____

_____

_____

_____

_____

People Change the Land
The Ultimate Book of Second Grade Skills, SV 9781419099533

Name _____   Date _____

Holiday Lineup

Directions Use the time line to complete the page.

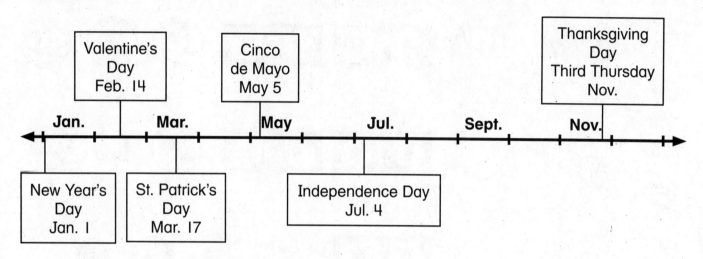

1. Which holiday is celebrated in May?

_____

2. In which month is St. Patrick's Day celebrated?

_____

3. What is the last month of the year? Write it on the time line.

_____

4. Labor Day is celebrated on the first Monday in September. Will it be closer to the September or October mark? Write it on the time line.

_____

5. In which month and on what day is your birthday? Write it on the time line.

_____

Time Line
The Ultimate Book of Second Grade Skills, SV 9781419099533

Costly Tools

Directions Draw a line to match each tool with its amount.

1.

A.

2.

B.

3.

C.

4.

D.

5.

E.

Directions Write the amounts from above in order from least to greatest.

6. _____   9. _____

7. _____   10. _____

8. _____

Money
The Ultimate Book of Second Grade Skills, SV 9781419099533

Book Talk

Directions **Answer the questions below to tell about your favorite book.**

1. What is the title of your favorite book? _____

_____

2. Who wrote your favorite book? _____

_____

3. What is your book about? Write three sentences or less to tell about

the book. _____

_____

_____

4. What part do you like best about the book? Draw a picture.

The Ultimate Book of Second Grade Skills, SV 9781419099533

Animal Groups

Directions Circle the animal names in the puzzle. Then write the name of each animal to tell which group it belongs in.

ant	snake	turtle	duck	giraffe	grasshopper
lion	lizard	man	ostrich	penguin	butterfly

g	s	e	r	t	o	s	t	r	i	c	h
i	n	c	d	f	k	n	u	l	o	p	e
r	a	b	u	t	t	e	r	f	l	y	m
a	k	d	c	o	t	a	t	p	i	d	a
f	e	l	k	s	e	z	l	b	o	u	n
f	l	i	z	a	r	d	e	a	n	t	s
e	p	e	n	g	u	i	n	m	k	a	t
g	r	a	s	s	h	o	p	p	e	r	p

1. **Mammals**

_____

_____

_____

2. **Birds**

_____

_____

3. **Reptiles**

_____

_____

_____

4. **Insects**

_____

_____

Animal Classification
The Ultimate Book of Second Grade Skills, SV 9781419099533

It's for You

Directions Write numbers <u>1</u> to <u>4</u> to show the order in which each product is made.

1.

_____

_____

_____

_____

2.

_____

_____

_____

_____

3.

_____

_____

_____

_____

The Ultimate Book of Second Grade Skills, SV 9781419099533

Name _____ Date _____

A Happy Ending

Directions) Read the words in the box. Which suffixes can be added to the ends of the words to make new words? Write the words in the correct column.

Remember

A suffix is a small word part added to the end of a root word that changes the word's meaning.

cloud   dark   help   quick   thank

1. **ful**   2. **less**   3. **ly**   4. **ness**

helpful   _____   _____   _____

_____   _____   _____   _____

_____

Directions) Write a word from the box above to complete each sentence.

5. Tia could see millions of stars in the _____ sky.

6. She made a campfire _____.

7. She was _____ for the light.

8. The campfire chased the _____ away.

9. Its heat was _____, too.

The Ultimate Book of Second Grade Skills, SV 9781419099533

Name _____   Date _____

Money Problems

Directions Add or subtract. Write the money symbols.

Remember

Add or subtract like you would a problem with three numbers. Remember to write the decimal point (.) and the dollar sign ($).

1. $1.64
   + 0.32

5. $2.34
   + 1.57

9. $6.25
   − 3.25

13. $6.45
    − 2.48

2. $1.82
   − 0.82

6. $3.21
   − 1.15

10. $8.39
    − 4.40

14. $5.00
    + 2.09

3. $2.45
   − 0.58

7. $5.00
   − 2.50

11. $7.50
    + 1.25

15. $3.75
    + 5.25

4. $3.60
   + 1.33

8. $4.75
   + 1.25

12. $9.00
    − 5.83

Name _____ Date _____

No Eating at This Table!

Directions Read the table of contents. Then answer the questions.

1. In which chapter would you learn about different birds?

_____

2. On what page does chapter 3 begin?

_____

3. Which chapter begins on page 12?

_____

4. Which chapter would you read if you wanted to buy a bird?

_____

5. Which chapter would you read if you wanted to know the name of a bird that you saw in your backyard?

_____

Facts About Mammals

Directions Unscramble the underlined letters to tell about mammals. Then circle the pictures of mammals.

1. Mammals have <u>arhi</u> on their bodies. _____

2. Mammals feed their babies <u>kilm</u>. _____

3. Mammals have <u>snugl</u> to breathe air. _____

4. Mammals give birth to <u>viel</u> babies. _____

5. Mammals are <u>ramw</u>-blooded. _____

Mammals
The Ultimate Book of Second Grade Skills, SV 9781419099533

Houses Around the World

Directions Draw a line to match each place with the house that is built there.

1.

A.

2.

B.

3.

C.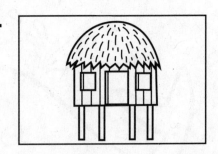

Name _____ Date _____

What's the Weather?

Directions What is the weather like? Use the picture clues to complete the puzzle.

1.

3.

5.

2.

4.

6.

Weather
The Ultimate Book of Second Grade Skills, SV 9781419099533

Name _____ Date _____

A Day at the Park

Directions Find the things that
have symmetry. Draw
the line of symmetry.

Remember

A line of symmetry divides
a shape in half so that each
side looks the exact same.

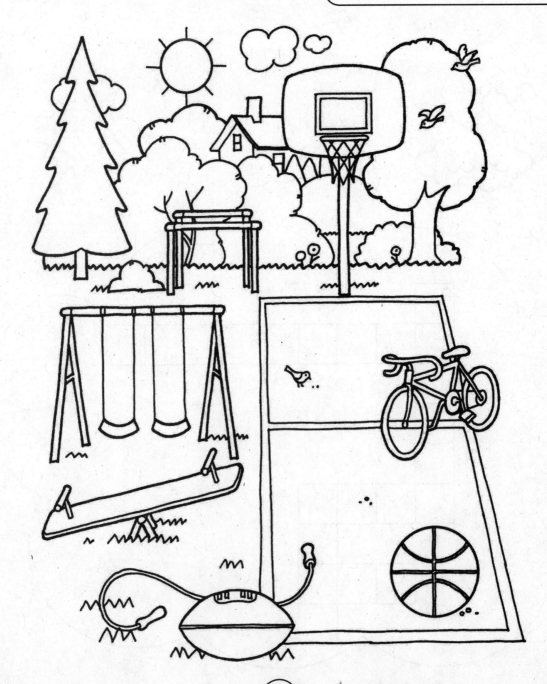

Treasure Map

Directions Read the story. Write an ending that could really happen. Then write another ending that is make-believe.

Rick had found an old map in his grandmother's attic. He thought it would be fun to hunt for the place shown on the map. But Rick did not think he would find anything. When Rick dug into the ground, he was surprised to uncover an old box. Slowly, Rick opened the lid.

Real Ending

_____

_____

_____

_____

Make-Believe Ending

_____

_____

_____

_____

The Ultimate Book of Second Grade Skills, SV 9781419099533

Name _____   Date _____

Planet Play

Directions Read each clue. Write the name of the planet.

Mercury   Venus   Earth   Mars   Jupiter   Saturn   Uranus Neptune

1. I am the largest planet. _____

2. I have red soil. _____

3. I am the second planet from the sun. _____

4. I have many rings and moons. _____

5. I have rings and spin on my side. _____

6. I am the smallest planet. _____

7. I am the planet farthest from the sun. _____

8. I have air and water. _____

Our World

Directions Look at the map. Answer the questions.

THE WORLD

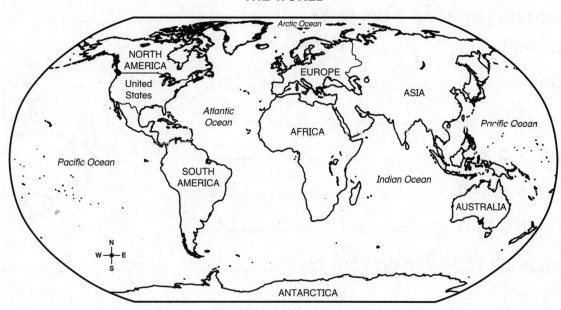

1. What are the names of the seven continents?

_____   _____

_____   _____

_____   _____

_____

2. What are the names of the four oceans?

_____   _____

_____   _____

3. On which continent do you live?

_____

Name _____ Date _____

Fun with Words

Directions Follow the directions to build each word. Write the last word to answer each riddle.

1. Where do you keep a pet fish? _____
   Start with: **desk**

   Change **e** to **i**: _____

   Change **i** to **u**: _____

   Change **d** to **t**: _____

   Change **u** to **a**: _____

   Change **s** to **n**: _____

2. What don't you want on your car? _____
   Start with: **want**

   Change **a** to **e**: _____

   Change **n** to **s**: _____

   Change **w** to **v**: _____

   Change **s** to **n**: _____

   Change **v** to **d**: _____

3. What is a good thing to keep in a bank? _____
   Start with: **hand**

   Change **h** to **l**: _____

   Change **a** to **e**: _____

   Change **l** to **b**: _____

   Change **d** to **t**: _____

   Change **b** to **c**: _____

          Final Blends
The Ultimate Book of Second Grade Skills, SV 9781419099533

Name _____   Date _____

The Shapes Around You

Directions Color the objects that match each shape.

1.

2.

3.

4.

5.

Same and Different

Directions Read the paragraph. Then answer the questions.

A firefighter and a police officer are community helpers. They both keep people safe. But the jobs of these helpers are very different. A firefighter puts out fires. A police officer makes sure that people follow the rules.

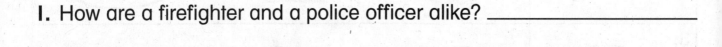

1. How are a firefighter and a police officer alike? _____

_____

2. How are a firefighter and a police officer different? _____

_____

Directions Look at the two dogs. Write sentences to tell how they are alike. Write sentences to tell how they are different.

_____

_____

_____

Compare and Contrast
The Ultimate Book of Second Grade Skills, SV 9781419099533

Turning Earth

Directions **Look at the picture. Circle the word or words that complete each sentence.**

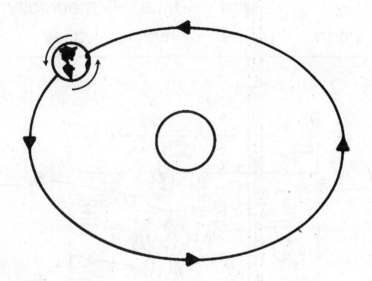

I. The Earth spins around once each _____.

day   week

2. The Earth's turning gives us _____.

summer and winter   day and night

3. The Earth moves around the sun once each _____.

month   year

4. The Earth's turning around the sun gives us _____.

seasons   snow and rain

The Ultimate Book of Second Grade Skills, SV 9781419099533

Name _____   Date _____

Land and Water

Directions Write a word from the box to label the map.

hills	island	lake	mountains
ocean	plains	river	valley

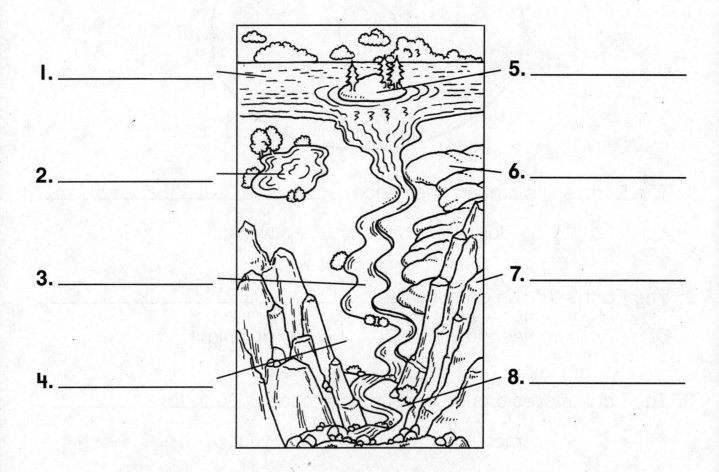

1. _____   5. _____

2. _____   6. _____

3. _____   7. _____

4. _____   8. _____

Name _____ Date _____

Getting to the End

Directions Write **.** or **?** or **!** to complete each sentence.

1. Jess walked her dog Jazz in the park ____

2. Do you know what happened ____

3. Jazz saw a cat ____

4. Jazz raced after the cat ____

5. Jess yelled, "Stop ____"

6. Do you think that Jazz stopped ____

7. No, Jazz did not stop ____

8. Jess had to run to keep up with her dog ____

9. How funny Jess looked ____

Ending Punctuation
The Ultimate Book of Second Grade Skills, SV 9781419099533

These Patterns Rule

Directions Look for a pattern. Write two more numbers to complete the pattern. Then write the rule.

1.  25 27 29 31

Rule: _____

2. 84 81 78 75

Rule: _____

3. 70 60 50 40

Rule: _____

4. 25 50 75 100

Rule: _____

5. 565 570 575 580

Rule: _____

The Ultimate Book of Second Grade Skills, SV 9781419099533

Name _____ Date _____

Friendly Writing

Directions Friendly letters have many parts. Use the lines below to create a letter to a friend.

Remember
Friendly letters have a date, greeting, body, closing, and signature.

(Date) _____

(Greeting) _____ ,

(Body) _____

_____

_____

_____

_____

_____

(Closing) _____ ,

(Signature) _____

Name _____ Date _____

Shadow Play

Directions Draw the sun in each picture.

1.	2.	3.

Directions Draw three pictures to show how your shadow changes.

4.	5.	6.

Shadow Cycles
The Ultimate Book of Second Grade Skills, SV 9781419099533

Name _____ Date _____

Which Way?

Directions Use the words from the box to label the compass rose. Then use the map to answer the questions.

north
east
south
west

1. _____

2. _____ 3. _____

4. _____

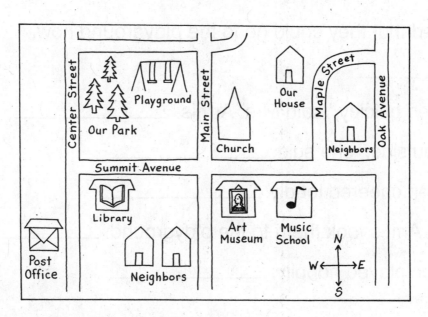

5. What is east of the art museum?

_____

6. What building is on the west side of town?

_____

7. What is north of the library and neighbors' houses?

_____

Name _____ Date _____

Time for the Playground

Directions Underline the adverb in each sentence. Then write <u>how</u>, <u>when</u>, or <u>where</u>.

Remember

An adverb describes a verb. It tells how, when, or where. Many adverbs end in <u>ly</u>.

1. It was early in the morning. _____

2. The children waited quietly. _____

3. They hoped that they could go to the playground now. _____

4. "You worked quickly," said Mrs. Armis. _____

5. "Let's go outside," she said. _____

6. The children cheered loudly. _____

7. Then Mrs. Armis took them to the playground. _____

8. The children played happily. _____

Catch a Train

Directions Write the number of the train leaving at the time shown on the clock.

Departing Times	
Train 23	2:00
Train 16	3:30
Train 11	10:30
Train 102	4:00
Train 37	12:30
Train 54	9:00

1.

Train _____

2.

Train _____

3.

Train _____

4.

Train _____

5.

Train _____

6.

Train _____

The Ultimate Book of Second Grade Skills, SV 9781419099533

Name _____ Date _____

All About the Moon Festival

Directions) Read the paragraph. Then write story details in the circles.

The Moon Festival is a big holiday in China. People celebrate it on August 15 each year. That is when the moon is big and bright. People wait until the moon rises high in the sky. They sing songs about the moon. They tell stories about it, too. Everyone eats small cakes. The cakes are filled with dates and nuts.

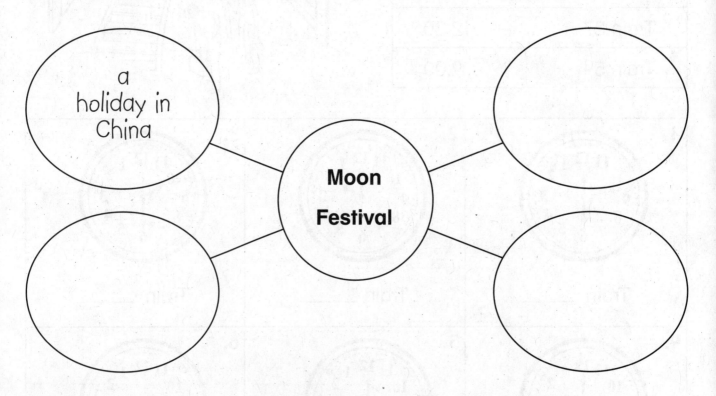

a holiday in China

Moon Festival

Directions) Write one or two sentences that tell about the paragraph above.

_____

_____

Summarize
The Ultimate Book of Second Grade Skills, SV 9781419099533

Name _____ Date _____

Water Water Everywhere

Directions Write a word from the box to label the water cycle.

cloud   evaporate   ocean   rain   sun

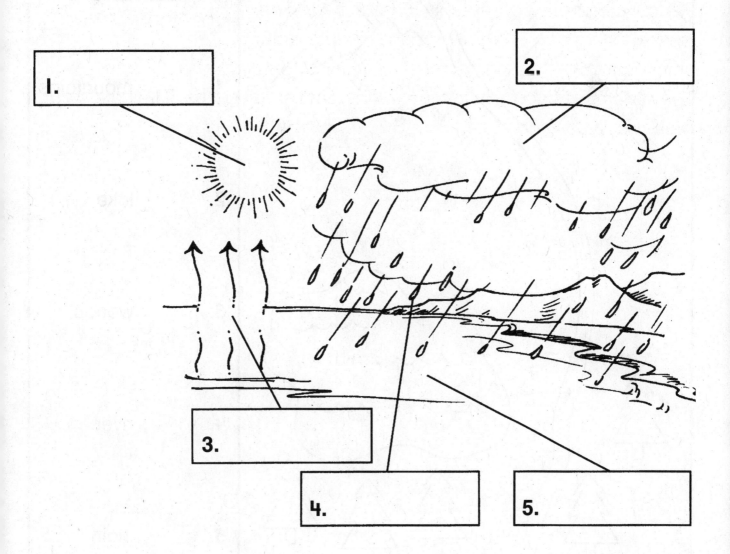

1.

2.

3.

4.

5.

Water Cycle
The Ultimate Book of Second Grade Skills, SV 9781419099533

The Key to Maps

Directions Draw symbols to complete the map key.

Map Key

1. mountains

2. lake

3. woods

4. river

5. plain

Name _____   Date _____

Fruit Graph

Directions **Look at the graph. Then answer the questions.**

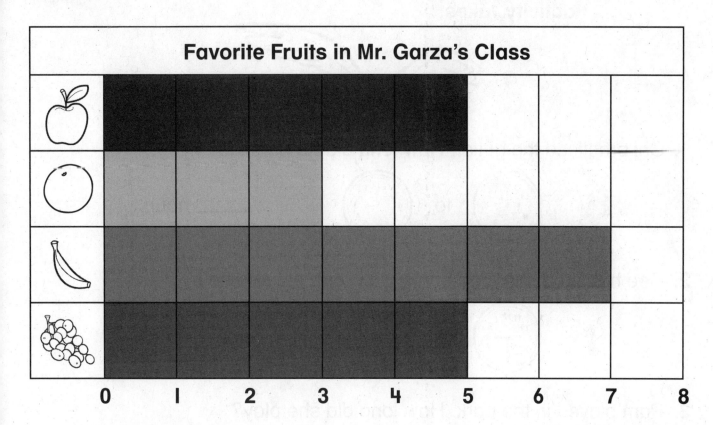

Favorite Fruits in Mr. Garza's Class

1. Which fruit did the most children like? _____

2. Which fruit was the least favorite? _____

3. Which fruits got the same number of votes?

   _____

4. How many more children liked bananas than oranges? _____

5. How many children are in Mr. Garza's class? _____

Graph
The Ultimate Book of Second Grade Skills, SV 9781419099533

Name _____ **Date** _____

Time Flies

Directions Look at each pair of clocks. Write the time each activity takes.

1. Chi practiced the guitar. How long did he practice?

 to _____ hours

2. Dee helped at the food bank. How long did she help?

 to _____ hours

3. Pam played in the park. How long did she play?

 to _____ hours

4. Leo worked in the yard with his dad. How long did he work?

 to _____ hours

5. Leanne went to the fair. How long was she there?

 to _____ hours

Plant Parts

Directions **Unscramble the letters to name plant parts.**

1. A <u>otor</u> helps the plant get water. _____

2. A <u>patel</u> gets the birds and bees to come. _____

3. A <u>feal</u> uses sunlight to make food. _____

4. The <u>mets</u> gets water to the leaves and flowers. _____

Directions **Use the words above to label the flower.**

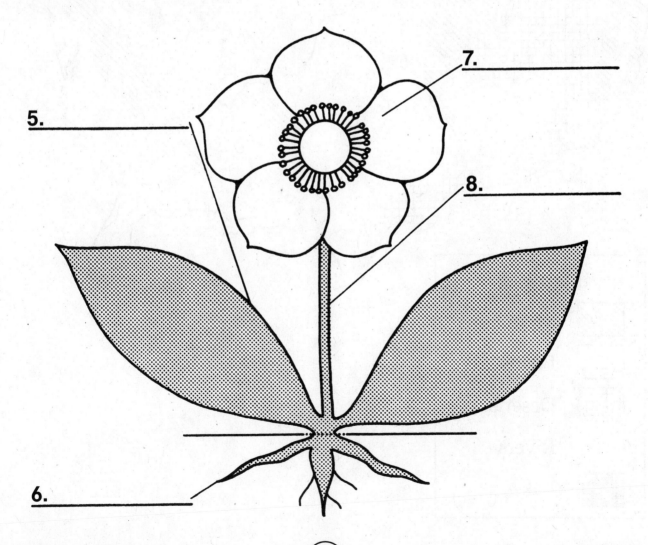

5. _____

6. _____

7. _____

8. _____

The Ultimate Book of Second Grade Skills, SV 9781419099533

One More Map

Directions Use crayons to color the symbols in the map key.
Then follow the map key to color the land and water
on the map.

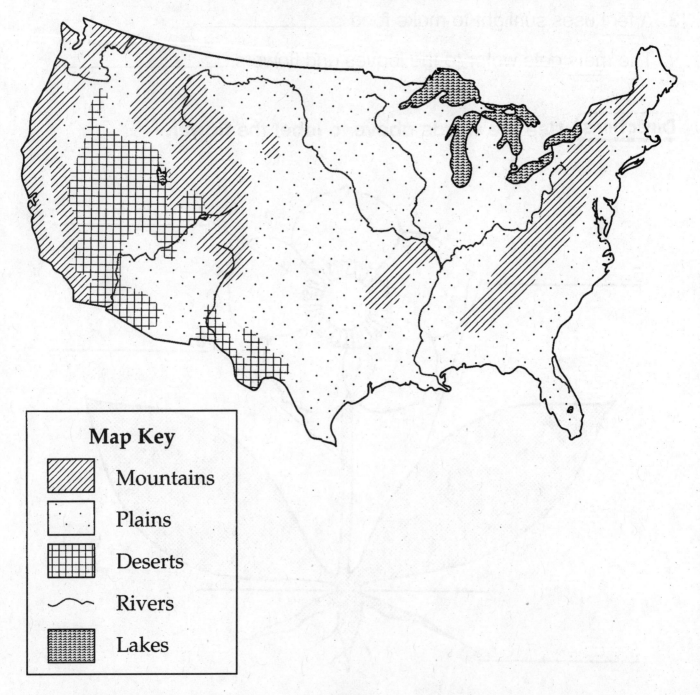

Map Key

Mountains

Plains

Deserts

Rivers

Lakes

The Ultimate Book of Second Grade Skills, SV 9781419099533
Map

Word Sounds

Directions Draw lines to match the thing with its sound word.

1.

whoosh

2.

moo

3.

pop

4.

sizzle

5.

clang

6.

buzz

Onomatopoeia
The Ultimate Book of Second Grade Skills, SV 9781419099533

Compute with the Calculator

Directions Estimate each sum or difference. Then use a calculator to find the answer.

Remember

To estimate, round numbers ending in 5 and higher up. Round numbers 4 and lower down.

$$\begin{array}{r} 29 \\ + \ 18 \\ \hline \end{array}$$

Estimate: _50_

Calculator: _47_

2 9 + 1 8 = 4 7

I.
$$\begin{array}{r} 42 \\ + \ 21 \\ \hline \end{array}$$

Estimate: _____

Calculator: _____

2.
$$\begin{array}{r} 97 \\ + \ 38 \\ \hline \end{array}$$

Estimate: _____

Calculator: _____

3.
$$\begin{array}{r} 54 \\ - \ 22 \\ \hline \end{array}$$

Estimate: _____

Calculator: _____

4.
$$\begin{array}{r} 724 \\ - \ 391 \\ \hline \end{array}$$

Estimate: _____

Calculator: _____

5.
$$\begin{array}{r} 658 \\ + \ 240 \\ \hline \end{array}$$

Estimate: _____

Calculator: _____

6.
$$\begin{array}{r} 931 \\ - \ 585 \\ \hline \end{array}$$

Estimate: _____

Calculator: _____

7.
$$\begin{array}{r} 608 \\ - \ 236 \\ \hline \end{array}$$

Estimate: _____

Calculator: _____

8.
$$\begin{array}{r} 271 \\ + \ 49 \\ \hline \end{array}$$

Estimate: _____

Calculator: _____

9.
$$\begin{array}{r} 589 \\ + \ 320 \\ \hline \end{array}$$

Estimate: _____

Calculator: _____

Calculator
The Ultimate Book of Second Grade Skills, SV 9781419099533

Ladybug Opposites

Directions Color the ladybugs that have words that are opposite in meaning. On the remaining ladybugs, cross out one word. Write a word that has an opposite meaning.

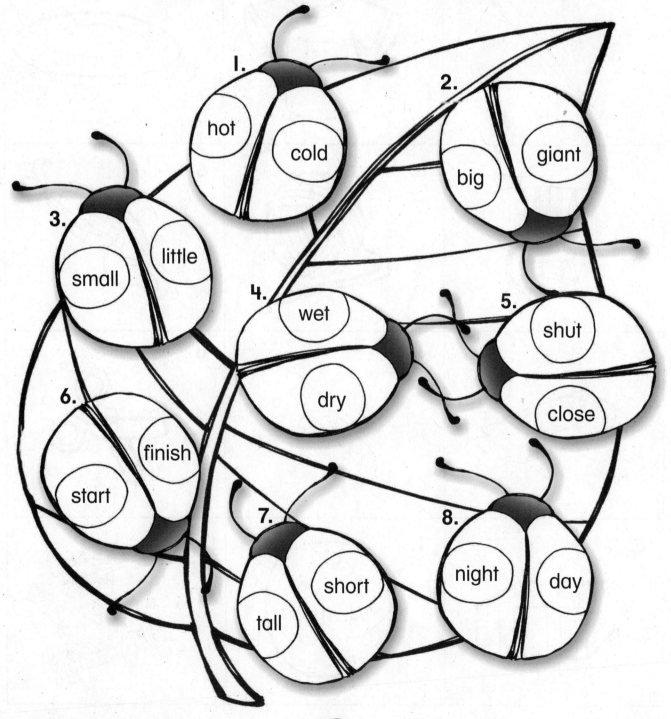

1. hot / cold
2. big / giant
3. small / little
4. wet / dry
5. shut / close
6. start / finish
7. short / tall
8. night / day

Antonyms
The Ultimate Book of Second Grade Skills, SV 9781419099533

Name _____ Date _____

Made from Plants

Directions Color the things that come from plants.

1. 	2. 	3. 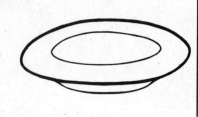
4. 	5. 	6. 
7. 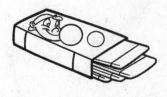	8. 	9. 
10. 	11. 	12. 

Products from Plants
The Ultimate Book of Second Grade Skills, SV 9781419099533

Name _____ Date _____

Around the Park

Directions Look at the picture. Answer the questions.

1. What are three things made by people?

_____

_____

_____

2. What are three things from nature?

_____

_____

_____

People Make Things
The Ultimate Book of Second Grade Skills, SV 9781419099533

Watch These Words

Directions Read each sentence. Circle the words that sound alike. Then find the words in a dictionary. Write the meaning of each word.

Remember
Homophones are words that sound alike, but they have different spellings and meanings.

I. Close the drawer after you put your clothes away.

_____

_____

2. Where are you going to wear that blue shirt?

_____

_____

3. They're going to get their clothes from over there.

_____

_____

4. Which two shirts are you going to buy?

_____

_____

Name _____ Date _____

Time to Multiply

Directions Complete the number sentences.

1.

2 + 2 + 2 = ___6___

3 equal groups of 2 = ___6___

___3___ × 2 = ___6___

2.

2 + 2 + 2 + 2 = _____

4 equal groups of 2 = _____

_____ × 2 = _____

3.

3 + 3 = _____

2 equal groups of 3 = _____

_____ × 3 = _____

4.

3 + 3 + 3 = _____

3 equal groups of 3 = _____

_____ × 3 = _____

5.

4 + 4 = _____

2 equal groups of 4 = _____

_____ × 4 = _____

6.

4 + 4 + 4 = _____

3 equal groups of 4 = _____

_____ × 4 = _____

Multiplication
The Ultimate Book of Second Grade Skills, SV 9781419099533

Get a Clue

1. I have legs, but I cannot walk. I have arms, but I cannot hug. I have a back, too. What am I?

child   table   chair

2. I am a fruit. I am round. You peel me to eat me. Be careful when you take a bite. I am very sweet and juicy. What am I?

orange   apple   banana

3. I am a machine. I have keys, but no locks. A mouse stays near me. What am I?

piano   computer   camera

4. I make music. You blow into me to make sounds. People hold me out to the side when they play me. What am I?

drum   flute   horn

Name _____ Date _____

These States Matter

Directions Look at the pictures.
Write <u>S</u> under the solids.
Write <u>L</u> under the liquids.
Write <u>G</u> under the gases.

Remember
A solid holds its shape. A liquid takes the shape of the container. A gas takes the shape of the container, too. Yet you cannot see a gas.

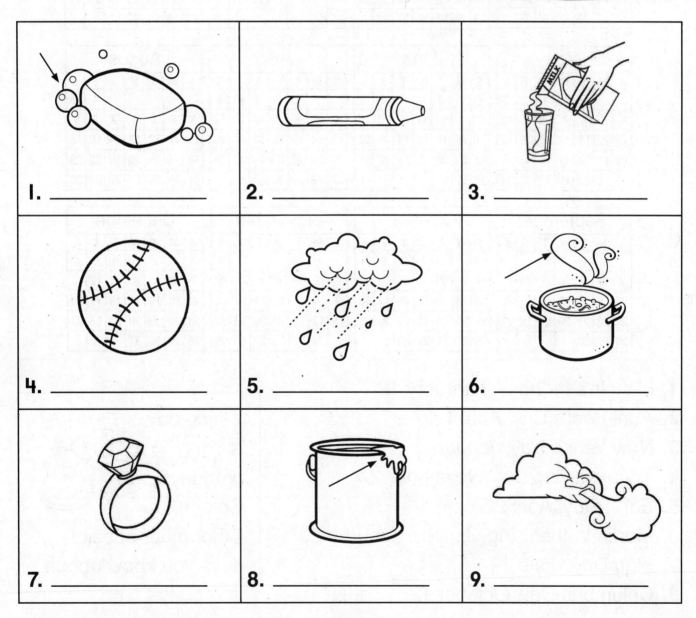

1. _____

2. _____

3. _____

4. _____

5. _____

6. _____

7. _____

8. _____

9. _____

Matter
The Ultimate Book of Second Grade Skills, SV 9781419099533

Name _____   Date _____

Special Days

Directions Look at the calendar. Then look at the dates of the special days. Color the dates on the calendar.

January
S	M	T	W	T	F	S
		1	2	3	4	
5	6	7	8	9	10	11
12	13	14	15	16	17	18
19	20	21	22	23	24	25
26	27	28	29	30	31	

February
S	M	T	W	T	F	S
						1
2	3	4	5	6	7	8
9	10	11	12	13	14	15
16	17	18	19	20	21	22
23	24	25	26	27	28	

March
S	M	T	W	T	F	S
						1
2	3	4	5	6	7	8
9	10	11	12	13	14	15
16	17	18	19	20	21	22
23/30	24/31	25	26	27	28	29

April
S	M	T	W	T	F	S
		1	2	3	4	5
6	7	8	9	10	11	12
13	14	15	16	17	18	19
20	21	22	23	24	25	26
27	28	29	30			

May
S	M	T	W	T	F	S
				1	2	3
4	5	6	7	8	9	10
11	12	13	14	15	16	17
18	19	20	21	22	23	24
25	26	27	28	29	30	31

June
S	M	T	W	T	F	S
1	2	3	4	5	6	7
8	9	10	11	12	13	14
15	16	17	18	19	20	21
22	23	24	25	26	27	28
29	30					

July
S	M	T	W	T	F	S
		1	2	3	4	5
6	7	8	9	10	11	12
13	14	15	16	17	18	19
20	21	22	23	24	25	26
27	28	29	30	31		

August
S	M	T	W	T	F	S
					1	2
3	4	5	6	7	8	9
10	11	12	13	14	15	16
17	18	19	20	21	22	23
24/31	25	26	27	28	29	30

September
S	M	T	W	T	F	S
	1	2	3	4	5	6
7	8	9	10	11	12	13
14	15	16	17	18	19	20
21	22	23	24	25	26	27
28	29	30				

October
S	M	T	W	T	F	S
			1	2	3	4
5	6	7	8	9	10	11
12	13	14	15	16	17	18
19	20	21	22	23	24	25
26	27	28	29	30	31	

November
S	M	T	W	T	F	S
						1
2	3	4	5	6	7	8
9	10	11	12	13	14	15
16	17	18	19	20	21	22
23/30	24	25	26	27	28	29

December
S	M	T	W	T	F	S
	1	2	3	4	5	6
7	8	9	10	11	12	13
14	15	16	17	18	19	20
21	22	23	24	25	26	27
28	29	30	31			

1. Lincoln's birthday, February 12
2. April Fool's Day, April 1
3. New Year's Day, January 1
4. Thanksgiving Day, November 27
5. Earth Day, April 22
6. Martin Luther King, Jr. Day, January 20
7. Flag Day, June 14
8. Columbus Day, October 12

Which day is your birthday? Color it. Color other special days you know about.

Calendar
The Ultimate Book of Second Grade Skills, SV 9781419099533

Name _____ Date _____

What Are You Saying?

Directions Tell what each sentence means.

1. The clothes on the line danced in the wind.

_____

_____

2. The suitcase was as heavy as an elephant.

_____

_____

3. The office was a cold as a freezer.

_____

_____

4. The children were as busy as beavers.

_____

_____

5. The bed was as hard as a rock.

_____

_____

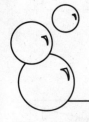

Making Groups

Directions Follow the directions. Then complete the sentences.

1.

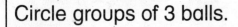

Circle groups of 3 balls.

There are ___6___ balls in all.

There are ___3___ balls in each group.

There are ___2___ groups of balls.

___6___ ÷ 3 = ___2___

2.

Circle groups of 4 balls.

There are _____ balls in all.

There are _____ balls in each group.

There are _____ groups of balls.

_____ ÷ 4 = _____

3.

Circle groups of 3 balls.

There are _____ balls in all.

There are _____ balls in each group.

There are _____ groups of balls.

_____ ÷ 3 = _____

4.

Circle groups of 4 balls.

There are _____ balls in all.

There are _____ balls in each group.

There are _____ groups of balls.

_____ ÷ 4 = _____

The Ultimate Book of Second Grade Skills, SV 9781419099533

Name _____ Date _____

It's a Fact

Directions **Write F if the sentence tells a fact. Write O if the sentence tells an opinion.**

1. _____ Wolves are part of the dog family.

2. _____ Wolves talk to each other by barking, growling, and howling.

3. _____ Ann thinks wolves are beautiful animals.

4. _____ The gray wolves are the prettiest.

5. _____ Wolves live together in packs.

6. _____ Wolves are the meanest animals.

Directions **Which animal do you like best? Write two facts and two opinions about the animal.**

Facts

_____

_____

_____

Opinions

_____

_____

_____

Mix It Up

Directions Look at the pictures.
Separate the things
in these mixtures.
Draw pictures.

Remember

A mixture is made by
combining several things.
The things in a mixture
can be separated.

1.

2.

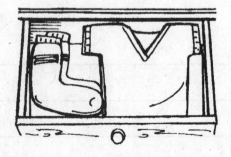

3.

The Ultimate Book of Second Grade Skills, SV 9781419099533

Name _____ Date _____

Getting to Know Some Presidents

Directions Write <u>yes</u> in the column that shows which president the sentence tells about. Some sentences may be about both presidents.

Fact	George Washington	Abraham Lincoln
1. I was the first president of the United States.		
2. I was born in February.		
3. I carried important papers in my tall hat.		
4. I was a general in the army.		
5. My picture is on money.		
6. I lived in a log cabin as a boy.		
7. There is a monument in Washington, D. C., with my name on it.		
8. I had false teeth.		

Washington and Lincoln
The Ultimate Book of Second Grade Skills, SV 9781419099533

Name _____ Date _____

Just Ducky

Directions **Write is or are to complete each sentence.**

1. Three ducks _____ swimming in the lake.

2. Two more ducks _____ going into the water.

3. One duck _____ looking for fish.

4. A boy and his dog _____ walking by the lake.

5. The dog _____ barking at the ducks.

6. Now the dog _____ jumping into the lake.

7. All the ducks _____ flying away.

8. The dog _____ proud of himself.

Verbs Is and Are
The Ultimate Book of Second Grade Skills, SV 9781419099533

Name _____ Date _____

Check a Dictionary

Directions Look at the dictionary pronunciation
key. Then circle the word that matches
the pronunciation.

---

mi·crobe |mī′krōb′| *n.* An organism too tiny to be seen
except with a microscope, especially one of the bacteria
that cause disease; germ.

---

a	add	i	it	o͞o	took	oi	oil
ā	ace	ī	ice	o͞o	pool	ou	pout
â	care	o	odd	u	up	ng	ring
ä	palm	ō	open	û	burn	th	thin
e	end	ô	order	yo͞o	fuse	t͟h	this
ē	equal					zh	vision

ə = { a in *above*   e in *sicken*   i in *possible*
       o in *melon*   u in *circus* }

---

1. (lo͝okt)   locked   lost   looked

2. (frend)   fried   friend   freed

3. (doun)   down   done   dune

4. (flou′ ûr)   floor   flavor   flower

5. (vīn)   van   vane   vine

6. (tīt)   tight   thought   tilt

7. (pûr′ fyo͞om)   perfume   perform   perfect

8. (ârz)   are   ears   airs

Dictionary Skills
The Ultimate Book of Second Grade Skills, SV 9781419099533

Story Corner

How the Elephant Got His Trunk

One day long ago, Elephant came to a pond to drink the cool water. He saw Crocodile taking a nap. Elephant and Crocodile often liked to tease each other. So Elephant decided to play a trick on Crocodile.

While Crocodile was sleeping, Elephant put some mud into Crocodile's ears. Elephant thought to himself how surprised Crocodile would be when he woke up and could not hear.

After a while, Elephant woke Crocodile. Elephant said, "How are you today, Crocodile?" Elephant seemed only to move his mouth as if he were speaking. Now, Crocodile was clever, and he realized what Elephant had done. So he decided to play his own trick on Elephant.

Crocodile said, "I can't hear you. Please come closer."

When Elephant got close enough, Crocodile snapped with his jaws and grabbed Elephant's tiny nose. Elephant pulled and pulled to try to get away. The more Elephant pulled, the more his nose stretched.

In the end, Elephant pulled free, but not before his nose stretched into a long trunk. That is why, to this day, elephants have long trunks.

Story Corner Questions

Directions Darken the circle by the word or words that best answer each question.

1. What kind of nose does Elephant have at the beginning of the story?

   ○ long   ○ large
   ○ small   ○ pointy

2. How does Elephant trick Crocodile?

   ○ He splashes Crocodile with water.
   ○ He snaps at Crocodile's nose.
   ○ He pulls Crocodile's tail.
   ○ He puts mud in Crocodile's ears.

3. What does Crocodile do to get even with Elephant?

   ○ He tells Elephant a joke.
   ○ He pulls Elephant's tail.
   ○ He grabs Elephant's nose.
   ○ He puts mud on Elephant's nose.

4. How does Elephant's nose change?

   ○ It gets longer.   ○ It gets smaller.
   ○ It gets fatter.   ○ It gets wider.

5. How is an elephant today different from Elephant at the beginning of the story?

   ○ It has a trunk.   ○ It has strong legs.
   ○ It is clever.   ○ It has large ears.

Congratulations,

_____!

You did a FIRST RATE job

on these SECOND GRADE skills!

1
Head
of the Class

Certificate
The Ultimate Book of Second Grade Skills, SV 9781419099533

Answer Key

Page 11
Check page for appropriate work.

Page 12
Check page for appropriate work.

Page 13
Check page for appropriate work.

Page 14
1. Color the baseball cap.
2. Color the tennis shoe.
3. Color the large doghouse.

Page 15
1. T, C
2. L, H
3. E, L
4. S, W
5. W, T
6. A, F
7. R, D
8. K, F
9. Q, I
10. S, H
Riddle: THE STARFISH

Page 16
1. 7
2. 4
3. 9
4. 8
5. 8
6. 9
7. 10
8. 8
9. 4
10. 9
11. 8
12. 7
13. 7
14. 7
15. 10
16. 5
17. 6
18. 7
19. 10
20. 6

Page 17
1. b
2. j
3. p
4. l
5. v
6. h
7. c
8. t
9. r
10. w
11. s
12. qu
13. d
14. g
15. m

Page 18
1. red
2. orange
3. pink
4. green
5. blue
6. gold
7. yellow
Sentence: rainbow

Page 19
1. 6
2. 4
3. 3
4. 5
5. 6
6. 3
7. 3
8. 5
9. 4
10. 5
11. 1
12. 0
13. 2
14. 4
15. 8

Page 20
1. v
2. x
3. l
4. m
5. f
6. r
7. k
8. t
9. n
10. p
11. d
12. s
13. g
14. b
15. t

Page 21
Check page for appropriate work.
1. corn
2. bird
3. car
4. hat
5. pool

Page 22
1. 3
2. 0
3. 8
4. 9
5. 6
6. 8
7. 3
8. 4
9. 8
10. 10
11. 4
12. 9
13. 3
14. 5
15. 5
16. 7
17. 8
18. 9

Page 23
1. m
2. r
3. p
4. z
5. v
6. b
7. n
8. x
9. g
10. d
11. d
12. m

Page 24
1. 2, 1, 3; air, bat, cat
2. 3, 1, 2; mail, neck, owl
3. 3, 2, 1; rock, sea, top
4. 3, 1, 2; us, vase, well
5. 2, 3, 1; x-ray, yes, zoo
6. 1, 3, 2; hat, in, jump
7. 2, 3, 1; dog, egg, fish

Page 25
1. $6 + 3 = 9$
   $3 + 6 = 9$
   $9 - 3 = 6$
   $9 - 6 = 3$
2. $5 + 2 = 7$
   $2 + 5 = 7$
   $7 - 5 = 2$
   $7 - 2 = 5$
3. $2 + 4 = 6$
   $4 + 2 = 6$
   $6 - 4 = 2$
   $6 - 2 = 4$
4. $7 + 3 = 10$
   $3 + 7 = 10$
   $10 - 7 = 3$
   $10 - 3 = 7$

Page 26
1. bat, cat
2. pan, fan
3. cap, map
4. mad, dad
5. tag, bag

Page 27
1. about a cup
2. more than a cup
3. less than a cup
4. about a cup
5. less than 5 gallons
6. more than 5 gallons
7. more than 5 gallons
8. more than 5 gallons

Page 28
1. yes
2. no
3. yes
4. yes
5. no
6. yes
7. no
8. yes
Answers will vary.

Page 29
1. jet, net
2. leg, beg
3. tent, cent
4. well, bell
5. vest, nest

Page 30
1. 2 tens, 5 ones; 25
2. 7 tens, 8 ones; 78
3. 4 tens, 4 ones; 44
4. 9 tens, 1 ones; 91
5. 6 tens, 6 ones; 66

Page 31
1. bat, hat, mat
2. men, hen, ten
3. bug, rug, hug

Page 32
1. wig, mitt, ship, fish
2. fin, pin
3. lips, lid, bridge
4. bib, pig, dig

Page 33
Check page for appropriate work.

Page 34
1. Color the bedroom.
2. Color the zoo.
3. Color the school.

Page 35
1. sock, rock
2. mop, top
3. box, fox
4. cot, pot
5. log, dog

Page 36
1. 12
2. 10
3. 11
4. 9
5. 12
6. 14
7. 12
8. 14
9. 11
10. 12
11. 12
12. 14
13. 13
14. 14
15. 11

Page 37
1. Fred is my friend.
2. He likes to run.
3. He had a race last week.
4. Fred was winning.
5. His shoelace came loose.
6. Fred tripped and fell.
7. Fred did not win the race.

Page 38
1. u
2. u
3. u
4. no answer
5. u
6. u
7. no answer
8. u
9. u
10. no answer
11. u
12. u
13. u
14. u
15. u
16. no answer

Page 39
1. 8
2. 8
3. 3
4. 4
5. 8
6. 6
7. 5
8. 4
9. 8
10. 5
11. 5
12. 8
13. 2
14. 7
15. 6
16. 7

Page 40
1. children, classroom
2. playground, school
3. teacher, ball
4. friends, swings
5. girl, rope
Person: children, teacher, friends, girl
Place: classroom, playground, school
Thing: ball, swings, rope

Page 41
1. bus, up
2. egg, web
3. pig, ink
4. ant, bat
5. mop, ox

The Ultimate Book of Second Grade Skills, SV 9781419099533

Page 42

1. 13	6. 14	11. 14
2. 11	7. 14	12. 17
3. 16	8. 12	13. 14
4. 11	9. 13	14. 15
5. 16	10. 18	

Page 43

1. boy	5. dresses
2. cats	6. rake
3. peaches	7. clown
4. lion	8. cars

Page 44

1. ducks, fun, mud
2. cat, sat, Pam's lap
3. Jen, went, get, pet, hen
4. dog, hops, on, log
5. Will, Jim's, big, fish, win

Page 45

Check page for appropriate work.

Page 46

One: wife, scarf, half, leaf, shelf, loaf, wolf
More Than One: wives, scarves, halves, leaves, shelves, loaves, wolves

Page 47

1. mane	5. cane
2. pane	6. vane
3. tape	7. cane
4. cape	8. tape
	9. pane

Page 48

1. 15	7. 13	13. 16
2. 6	8. 9	14. 18
3. 14	9. 14	15. 9
4. 9	10. 14	16. 7
5. 8	11. 9	17. 8
6. 9	12. 7	18. 17

Page 49

Check page for appropriate work.

Page 50

1. hay	5. jay
2. train	6. rake
3. pail	7. mail
4. cane	8. whale

Page 51

Color the ball with the correct number.

1. 17	5. 76	8. 3
2. 28	6. 96	9. 100
3. 34	7. 89	10. 66
4. 50		

Page 52

1. Leah reads a book.
2. The bird sits in a nest.
3. Anna gets on the bus.
4. Toys have been around for many years.

Page 53

Follow the path: meal, creep, green, neat, queen, jeep, heat, feel, seal, see, neat, eat

Page 54

1. 6 tens	4. 7 hundreds
2. 1 hundreds	5. 0 tens
3. 8 ones	6. 6 ones

Page 55

1. Color the jack-in-the-box.
2. Color the shell.

Page 56

1. funny	6. greed
2. me	7. money
3. squeal	8. valley
4. piggy	9. he
5. happy	10. empty

Page 57

1. <	7. >	12. >
2. >	8. >	13. >
3. >	9. <	14. >
4. <	10. >	15. <
5. >	11. <	16. <
6. <		

Page 58

1. rain, bow, rainbow
2. star, fish, starfish
3. foot, ball, football
4. bird, house, birdhouse

Page 59

1. dice	7. bike
2. no answer	8. pipe
3. nine	9. no answer
4. hive	10. dive
5. no answer	11. no answer
6. no answer	12. vine

Page 60

1. 9	6. 14	11. 18
2. 10	7. 14	12. 17
3. 8	8. 15	13. 18
4. 6	9. 10	14. 17
5. 13	10. 16	

Page 61

1. sad	5. hopped
2. sick	6. friend
3. sleep	7. house
4. yell	8. giggle

Page 62

1. Draw a pie on *lie*.
2. Draw a kite on *dry*.
3. Draw a kite on *try*.
4. Draw a pie on *die*.
5. Draw a kite on *my*.
6. Draw a kite on *tire*.
7. Draw a kite on *by*.
8. Draw a pie on *tie*.
Winner: Mike

Page 63

1. 15	7. 61	12. 50
2. 27	8. 59	13. 89
3. 38	9. 89	14. 77
4. 39	10. 97	15. 97
5. 49	11. 88	16. 86
6. 77		

Page 64

1. A	3. A	5. B
2. B	4. A	6. B

Page 65

Check page for appropriate work.
Answers will vary.
Message: See how my bright kite flies in the sky.

1. kite	3. my, sky
2. flies	4. bright

Page 66

1. 14	7. 42	12. 62
2. 23	8. 21	13. 50
3. 20	9. 51	14. 33
4. 41	10. 42	15. 11
5. 23	11. 22	16. 16
6. 33		

Page 67

1. eat	4. jump
2. run	5. throw
3. talk	6. ride

Circle 2, 4, 5, 6.
Check paragraph.

Page 68

1. rope	7. no answer
2. no answer	8. rose
3. cone	9. no answer
4. hose	10. nose
5. no answer	11. no answer
6. robe	12. globe

Page 69

1. 38	7. 11	12. 52
2. 41	8. 98	13. 64
3. 29	9. 89	14. 87
4. 40	10. 70	15. 10
5. 11	11. 46	16. 93
6. 89		

Page 70

1. noun	6. verb
2. verb	7. noun
3. verb	8. verb
4. noun	9. noun
5. noun	10. verb

Answers will vary.

Page 71

1. bow	4. snow
2. blow	5. crow
3. throw	6. low

Page 72

1. 24	6. 78	11. 87
2. 32	7. 93	12. 91
3. 40	8. 44	13. 81
4. 85	9. 62	14. 80
5. 51	10. 96	

Page 73

Possible answers:

1. zoom	5. speed
2. stroll	6. march
3. race	7. jogs
4. pedal	8. travels

Page 74

Check page for appropriate work.

1. cube	5. plume
2. cute	6. due
3. huge	7. blue
4. tube	8. glue

Page 75

1. 19	6. 8	11. 33
2. 17	7. 34	12. 39
3. 16	8. 39	13. 48
4. 28	9. 45	14. 3
5. 35	10. 19	

Page 76

1. nonfiction	3. fiction
2. poem	

Page 77

1. i	5. o	8. e
2. u	6. e	9. a
3. i	7. u	10. o
4. a		

Page 78

1. 31	7. 57	12. 70
2. 29	8. 90	13. 49
3. 27	9. 80	14. 82
4. 70	10. 44	15. 9
5. 29	11. 53	16. 66
6. 85		

Page 79

1. build sand castles on the beach.
2. wash up on the beach for us to find.
3. fly above the water.

The Ultimate Book of Second Grade Skills, SV 9781419099533

4. sticks to our feet.
5. swim far out in the ocean water.
6. subject; The ocean waves crash.
7. predicate; Boys dig a big hole
8. predicate; Jane reads under an umbrella.

Page 80
Bodies Growing: a, c, h
Learning Things: b, d, g
Being Responsible: e, f, i

Page 81
1. cent, mice, lace
2. cap, cat, cot
3. goat, gum, bag
4. giraffe, giant, cage
5. sun, sink, gas
6. rose, cheese, music
7. sugar, tissue, mission

Page 82
Color the following coins:
1. dime, nickel, penny
2. quarter, 3 pennies
3. quarter, nickel, 2 pennies
4. quarter, dime
5. quarter, dime, nickel, 3 pennies

Page 83
1. skipping   5. biking
2. walking   6. running
3. playing   7. hugging
4. talking
Riddle: skating

Page 84
Answers will vary.

Page 85
1. sp   5. st   9. sk
2. sn   6. sc   10. st
3. sk   7. sn   11. sl
4. sl   8. sp   12. sw

Page 86
1. 113, 313
2. 645, 845
3. 394, 594
4. 370, 570
5. 86, 286
6. 799, 999
7. <   10. <   13. >
8. >   11. <   14. >
9. >   12. <   15. <

Page 87
3, 2, 5, 1, 4
3, 1, 5, 2, 4

Page 88
1. wash   4. bed
2. teeth   5. lotion
3. food

Page 89
1. cr   5. gr   9. tr
2. br   6. fr   10. gr
3. tr   7. cr   11. fr
4. dr   8. br   12. pr

Page 90
1. 3 ounces   5. 15 pounds
2. 8 pounds   6. 10 pounds
3. 3 pounds   7. 1 pound
4. 2,000 pounds   8. 1 ton

Page 91
1. Tuesday: draw a line to *Tues.*
2. Sunday: draw a line to *Sun.*
3. Friday: draw a line to *Fri.*
4. Wednesday: draw a line to *Wed.*
5. Monday: draw a line to *Mon.*
6. Thursday: draw a line to *Thurs.*
7. Saturday: draw a line to *Sat.*
Calendar order: Sun., Mon., Tues., Wed., Thurs., Fri., Sat.

Page 92
1. B   2. A   3. A

Page 93
1. fl   5. cl   9. pl
2. gl   6. fl   10. sl
3. cl   7. bl   11. bl
4. gl   8. pl   12. sl

Page 94
1. star   5. rectangle
2. diamond   6. triangle
3. heart   7. square
4. circle   8. rhombus

Page 95
1. visited   5. learned
2. looked   6. paints
3. watched   7. wants
4. asked   8. hopes

Page 96
1. ham, corn, gum, bread
2. rain, grass, rose, soap
3. bug, book, rose, horse, barn
4. bird, shirt, yarn, dirt
5. horn, bark, chirp, purr, flute

Page 97
1. st   7. nd   12. st
2. nt   8. mp   13. nd
3. nd   9. sk   14. st
4. nt   10. nt   15. sk
5. sk   11. mp   16. nk
6. mp

Page 98
Draw a line to the following:
1. thermometer
2. measuring cup
3. clock
4. scale
5. calendar
6. ruler

Page 99
1. skating   4. closing
2. named   5. sneezed
3. liking   6. scored
Riddle: smiled

Page 100
Answers will vary.

Page 101
1. when   4. chick
2. shine   5. shop
3. thin   6. wheel
Answers will vary.

Page 102
1. 3   3. 6   5. 2
2. 4   4. 1

Page 103
1. Q
2. S
3. S
4. Q
5. S
6. What will Maria do when she gets back?
7. She will go to her drum lesson.
8. Maria wants to play in a band someday.

Page 104
Answers will vary for the second part of each item.
1. surprised   3. worried
2. mad   4. happy

Page 105
1. law
2. safe
3. clean
4. fair
5. Possible answer: Put trash in a trash can.
6. Possible answer: Follow signs when crossing the street.

Page 106
1. knight
2. wrench
3. gnaw
4. knee
5. wrist
6. sign
7. knife
8. gnome
9. write
10. knight, knee, knife
11. gnaw, sign, gnome
12. wrench, wrist, write

Page 107
Check page for appropriate work.

Page 108
Possible answers:
1. warm   4. hot
2. cold   5. hungry
3. two   6. cool

Page 109
1. summer   3. winter
2. fall   4. spring
Answers will vary.

Page 110
1. exit   3. walk
2. stop   4. no bikes
Answers will vary.

Page 111
1. porch
2. park
3. car
4. horse
5. fork
6. yarn
Riddle: popcorn

Page 112
1. 4   3. 14   5. 9
2. 8   4. 11

Page 113
1. tree
2. happily
3. see
4. me
5. red
6. head
7. said
8. fled

Page 114
Draw a line to the following:
1. *takes food into the body*
2. *crushes food and turns it into a thick liquid*
3. *tastes food and pushes it into the throat*

The Ultimate Book of Second Grade Skills, SV 9781419099533

4. *chews the food*
5. mouth
6. tongue
7. teeth
8. stomach

Page 115
Draw a line to the following:
1. *Take turns when playing games.*
2. *Wait your turn in line without playing.*
3. *Wear a helmet when riding a bike.*
Answers will vary.

Page 116
1. beach, bead, pea, seat
2. head, heavy, spread, thread
3. beach
4. heavy
5. spread
6. seat
7. head

Page 117
1. Draw a square.
2. Draw a rectangle.
3. Draw a circle.
4. Draw a triangle.

Page 118
Check page for appropriate work.
1. Lana is in North Carolina.
2. She is visiting her grandmother in Raleigh.
3. Lana's grandmother is Jan Washington.
4. Mrs. Washington lives on Oak Street.
5. Lana and her grandmother went to the North Carolina Zoo.
6. Lana will return to Topeka, Kansas, on Tuesday.
7. She will be happy to get back to her house on Park Street.
8. She knows Hill Elementary School will start in one week.
9. School will start on September 1.
10. Lana and her brother Lee will shop for school supplies.

Page 119
Check page for appropriate work.
1. enamel
2. roots
3. dentin

Page 120
1. community
2. money
3. tax
4. services
5. Possible answer: A firefighter puts out fires.
6. Possible answer: A judge makes sure people follow laws.
7. Possible answer: A teacher teaches children.

Page 121
1. book, cook, good, look, stood
2. goose, moon, room, tool, zoo
3. room
4. book
5. moon
6. look
7. good

Page 122
1. square   **4.** cylinder
2. rectangle   **5.** cube
3. circle   **6.** pyramid

Page 123
1. Circle 90° F.
2. Circle 30° F.
3. Circle 70° F.
4. 50° F
5. 60° F
6. 80° F
7. 12°
8. 95°
9. 34°
10. 72°

Page 124
1. choose
2. healthy
3. snacks
Answers will vary.

Page 125
Across   Down
4. leaders   **1.** vote
5. president   **2.** governor
                   3. mayor

Page 126
Seize the thief.

Page 127
1. Circle the square and heart.
2. Circle the rectangle and hexagon.
3. Circle the diamond and hexagon.
4. $\frac{1}{2}$

5. $\frac{1}{3}$
6. $\frac{1}{3}$
7. $\frac{2}{2}$
8. $\frac{2}{4}$
9. $\frac{3}{4}$
10. $\frac{3}{3}$

Page 128
1. C   **2.** B

Page 129
Answers will vary.

Page 130
1. erosion   **5.** ecology
2. trash   **6.** garbage
3. Earth   **7.** pollution
4. litter   **8.** recycle
Answers will vary.

Page 131
Across   Down
1. sleigh   **2.** eighteen
3. weight   **4.** neighbor
5. eight
6. neigh

Page 132
Check page for appropriate work.

Page 133
1. younger, young, youngest
2. longest, long, longer
3. bigger, biggest, big
4. tall, taller, tallest

Page 134
1. swim
2. skate
3. dance
4. run
5. jump
6. pedal
7. Possible answer: Exercise helps your heart and lungs grow strong. You want to make your heart beat faster. You want to get lots of air in your lungs.

Page 135
thaw, hawk, pause, straw
fawn, haul, claw, taught
1. hawk   **5.** claw
2. pause   **6.** haul
3. thaw   **7.** taught
4. fawn   **8.** straw

Page 136
Check page for appropriate work.

Page 137
1. Rita, Jess, and Tom went for a walk.
2. They put on coats, scarves, and mittens.
3. The friends saw a squirrel, deer, and raccoon along the way.
4. The leaves were turning red, orange, and yellow.
5. The hikers were tired, cold, and hungry when they got back home.
6. Rita fixed hot chocolate, cookies, and crackers to eat.
7. Rita asked, "Do you want to play games, sing songs, or watch TV?"
8. Rita, Jess, and Tom decided to do all three.

Page 138
Draw a line to the following:
1. D   **3.** A
2. C   **4.** B
Answers will vary.

Page 139
1. A, B, D   **5.** A, D
2. C, D   **6.** A, B, D
3. A, D   **7.** D
4. B, C, D   **8.** D

Page 140
1. ground
2. round
3. brown
4. wound
5. Wow, shouted
Answer: a watch

Page 141
1. red; There are more red gum balls.
2. blue; There are fewer blue gum balls.

Page 142
1. wasn't   **5.** haven't
2. didn't   **6.** don't
3. we're   **7.** it's
4. I'm   **8.** let's

Page 143
Draw a line to the following:
1. D or E   **4.** B
2. C   **5.** A
3. D or E

Page 144
1. services   **4.** both
2. both   **5.** both
3. both   **6.** services

Page 145
Check page for appropriate work.

Page 146
1. 7
2. 6
3. 5
4. 7 + 6 + 5 = 18
5. 18 cm
6. 4
7. 10
8. 4
9. 10
10. 4 + 10 + 4 + 10 = 28
11. 28 cm

Page 147
1. It was raining.
2. The box held supplies for a picnic.
3. Kim was happy. She got to have a picnic with Maria.

Page 148
Draw a line to the following:
1. B   3. A   5. D
2. E   4. C

Page 149
1. income
2. budget
3. savings
4. taxes
Circle the following: apartment rent, food, electricity, water, gas, taxes

Page 150
1. herd   4. bird
2. fern   5. shirt
3. nurse   6. purse

Page 151
1. 112   7. 711   12. 910
2. 150   8. 943   13. 362
3. 211   9. 977   14. 635
4. 352   10. 800   15. 807
5. 262   11. 575   16. 830
6. 505

Page 152
1. January   12. December
2. February   13. Jan.
3. March   14. Aug.
4. April   15. Oct.
5. May   16. Mar.
6. June   17. Sept.
7. July   18. Dec.
8. August   19. Nov.
9. September   20. Feb.
10. October   21. Apr.
11. November

Page 153
1. snake, raccoon, groundhog, worm, bear
2. wolf, rabbit, reindeer, fox
3. bat, butterfly, goose

Page 154
Answers will vary.

Page 155
1. flew   5. drew
2. new   6. blue
3. stew   7. due
4. glue   8. crew

Page 156
1. 129   7. 730   12. 715
2. 188   8. 795   13. 215
3. 267   9. 455   14. 209
4. 359   10. 360   15. 367
5. 402   11. 59   16. 332
6. 491

Page 157
People: Ryan, Mrs. Barton, Ryan
Places: Spring Mall, Shady Street, Rex Art Museum
Things: Saturday, Tuesday, June

Page 158
Check page for appropriate work.

Page 159
1. C   4. P   7. P
2. P   5. C   8. C
3. C   6. C   9. P

Page 160
Across   Down
2. unable   1. unfair
3. unhappy   3. unclean
5. rewrite   4. reuse
7. reread   6. retie
                 8. again
                 9. not

Page 161
1. 156   7. 500   12. 772
2. 183   8. 104   13. 905
3. 364   9. 197   14. 805
4. 573   10. 831   15. 507
5. 104   11. 231   16. 900
6. 392

Page 162
1. Circle the sad girl.
2. Circle the worried man.
3. Circle the surprised girl.

Page 163
Answers will vary.

Page 164
1. Possible answers: built buildings, made gardens, built fences
2. Possible answers: built cooking grills, built dock, added picnic tables

Page 165
Check page for appropriate work.
1. Cinco de Mayo
2. March
3. December
4. September
5. Answers will vary.

Page 166
1. C   5. D   8. $1.95
2. B   6. $1.37 9. $2.40
3. A   7. $1.56 10. $2.75
4. E

Page 167
Answers will vary.

Page 168
1. giraffe, lion, man
2. duck, ostrich, penguin
3. lizard, snake, turtle
4. ant, butterfly, grasshopper

Page 169
1. 1, 2, 3, 4   3. 3, 2, 4, 1
2. 4, 1, 3, 2

Page 170
1. helpful, thankful
2. cloudless, helpless, thankless
3. darkly, quickly
4. darkness, quickness
5. cloudless
6. quickly
7. thankful
8. darkness
9. helpful

Page 171
1. $1.96   6. $2.06   11. $8.75
2. $1.00   7. $2.50   12. $3.17
3. $1.87   8. $6.00   13. $3.97
4. $4.93   9. $3.00   14. $7.09
5. $3.91   10. $3.99   15. $9.00

Page 172
1. Chapter 2   4. Chapter 4
2. Page 10   5. Chapter 2
3. Chapter 4

Page 173
1. hair   4. live
2. milk   5. warm
3. lungs
Circle the following: tiger, bat, whale, dog, cow

Page 174
Draw a line to the following:
1. C   2. A   3. B

Page 175
1. rain   4. snow
2. clouds   5. wind
3. lightning 6. sun

Page 176
Draw a line of symmetry on the following: sun, evergreen tree, parallel bars, basketball goal, basketball, basketball court, swing set, football, seesaw

Page 177
Answers will vary.

Page 178
1. Jupiter   5. Uranus
2. Mars   6. Mercury
3. Venus   7. Neptune
4. Saturn   8. Earth

Page 179
1. North America, South America, Africa, Europe, Asia, Australia, Antarctica
2. Atlantic Ocean, Pacific Ocean, Arctic Ocean, Indian Ocean
3. North America

Page 180
1. disk, dusk, tusk, task, tank
2. went, west, vest, vent, dent
3. land, lend, bend, bent, cent

Page 181
Color the following:
1. candle, can
2. ice cube, block
3. globe, yarn ball
4. soap, book
5. funnel, party hat

Page 182
1. Both are community helpers. Both help keep people safe.
2. A firefighter puts out fires. A police officer makes sure people follow rules.
Possible answers: Each dog has 4 legs, 2 ears, 2 eyes, 1 tail, and 1 tongue. One dog has spots. One is fluffy. One dog is barking, and one is quiet.

Page 183
1. day   3. year
2. day and night 4. seasons

Answer Key
The Ultimate Book of Second Grade Skills, SV 9781419099533

Page 184
1. ocean   5. island
2. lake   6. hills
3. river   7. mountains
4. plains   8. valley

Page 185
Possible answers:
1. .   4. .   7. !
2. ?   5. !   8. .
3. .   6. ?   9. !

Page 186
1. 33, 35; add 2
2. 72, 69; subtract 3
3. 30, 20; subtract 10
4. 125, 150; add 25
5. 585, 590; add 5

Page 187
Answers will vary.

Page 188
Check page for appropriate work.

Page 189
1. north
2. west
3. east
4. south
5. Music School
6. Post Office
7. Park and Playground

Page 190
1. Underline *early;* when
2. Underline *quietly;* how
3. Underline *now;* when
4. Underline *quickly;* how
5. Underline *outside;* where
6. Underline *loudly;* how
7. Underline *then;* when
8. Underline *happily;* how

Page 191
1. 37   3. 41   5. 102
2. 23   4. 54   6. 16

Page 192
Check page for appropriate work.

Page 193
1. sun   4. rain
2. cloud   5. ocean
3. evaporate

Page 194
1. Possible answer: Children duplicate the mountain.
2. Possible answer: Children duplicate the wave.
3. Possible answer: Children duplicate the pine tree.

4. Possible answer: Children duplicate the curve.
5. Possible answer: Children duplicate the grass.

Page 195
1. banana
2. orange
3. apple and grapes
4. 4
5. 20

Page 196
1. 2   3. 3   5. 6
2. 1   4. 4

Page 197
1. root   5. leaf
2. petal   6. root
3. leaf   7. petal
4. stem   8. stem

Page 198
Check page for appropriate work.

Page 199
Draw a line to the following:
1. pop   4. sizzle
2. buzz   5. whoosh
3. moo   6. clang

Page 200
1. 60; 63   6. 300; 346
2. 140; 135   7. 400; 372
3. 30; 32   8. 350; 320
4. 300; 333   9. 900; 909
5. 900; 898

Page 201
1. Color the ladybug.
2. Possible answer: big, little
3. Possible answer: small, large
4. Color the ladybug.
5. Possible answer: open, close
6. Color the ladybug.
7. Color the ladybug.
8. Color the ladybug.

Page 202
Color 1, 2, 4, 6, 7, 8, 11, and 12.

Page 203
1. Possible answers: statue, bridge, baby carriage, car
2. Possible answers: rocks, clouds, birds, and water

Page 204
Check page for appropriate work.
1. close, clothes
2. where, wear

3. They're, their, there
4. two, to

Page 205
1. $2 + 2 + 2 = 6$
   3 equal groups of 2 = 6
   $3 \times 2 = 6$
2. $2 + 2 + 2 + 2 = 8$
   4 equal groups of 2 = 8
   $4 \times 2 = 8$
3. $3 + 3 = 6$
   2 equal groups of 3 = 6
   $2 \times 3 = 6$
4. $3 + 3 + 3 = 9$
   3 equal groups of 3 = 9
   $3 \times 3 = 9$
5. $4 + 4 = 8$
   2 equal groups of 4 = 8
   $2 \times 4 = 8$
6. $4 + 4 + 4 = 12$
   3 equal groups of 4 = 12
   $3 \times 4 = 12$

Page 206
1. chair   3. computer
2. orange   4. flute

Page 207
1. G   4. S   7. S
2. S   5. L   8. L
3. L   6. G   9. G

Page 208
Check page for appropriate work.

Page 209
1. The wind blew the clothes and made them move.
2. The suitcase was very heavy.
3. The office was very cold.
4. The children worked very hard.
5. The bed was stiff and uncomfortable.

Page 210
2. There are 8 balls in all. There are 4 balls in each group. There are 2 groups of balls. $8 \div 4 = 2$
3. There are 9 balls in all. There are 3 balls in each group. There are 3 groups of balls. $9 \div 3 = 3$
4. There are 12 balls in all. There are 4 balls in each group. There are 3 groups of balls. $12 \div 4 = 3$

Page 211
1. F   3. O   5. F
2. F   4. O   6. O
Answers will vary.

Page 212
1. Children draw lettuce, celery, carrots, and tomatoes.
2. Children draw apples, oranges, and grapes.
3. Children draw two socks and a shirt.

Page 213
1. Washington
2. Washington, Lincoln
3. Lincoln
4. Washington
5. Washington, Lincoln
6. Lincoln
7. Washington, Lincoln
8. Washington

Page 214
1. are   4. are   7. are
2. are   5. is   8. is
3. is   6. is

Page 215
1. looked   5. vine
2. friend   6. tight
3. down   7. perfume
4. flower   8. airs

Page 217
1. small
2. He puts mud in Crocodile's ears.
3. He grabs Elephant's nose.
4. It gets longer.
5. It has a trunk.

Answer Key
The Ultimate Book of Second Grade Skills, SV 9781419099533